Landscape
in Sussex

Colin Mitchell

S. B. Publications

*This book is dedicated to those who love the countryside
and seek to understand its meaning*

Cover photograph: The cliffs at Hastings Country Park.
Back cover: Wave-cut platform at Galley Hill.
Title page: Looking north from Cissbury, with the author in the foreground.

Edited by David Arscott at Pomegranate Press.

British Library Cataloguing-in Publication Data.
A catalogue record for this book is available from the British Library.

ISBN 1-85770-290-5

First published in 2004 by S.B. Publications, c/o 19 Grove Road, Seaford, East
Sussex BN25 1TP. Tel: 01323 893498.

Printed by

Contents

A BRIEF SUMMARY OF WEALDEN GEOLOGY

Sussex represents the southern part of the Weald, an east-west oriented oval anticline formed of alternating sediments ranging in age from Jurassic to Recent.

The central core is Wealden Sandstone, and this is surrounded in order by concentric bands of Weald Clay, Lower Greensand, Gault Clay and Chalk. The surface of all has been modified by later erosion and the local addition of superficial deposits.

The geological skeleton of the Weald was present at the end of the Tertiary period and was modified by the drainage system and changes in sea level which followed. The end of the Pliocene period saw a high sea level which cut the Calabrian bench across the higher ground. When the sea level dropped during the Ice Age, rivers drained north and south off the Wealden oval. As they cut down they developed tributaries along the trends of the strata. Since then the drainage pattern has been maintained, except for some river captures. The higher interglacial sea levels cut horizontal benches on the hills and caused the rivers to build corresponding terraces in their valleys.

Since the retreat of the ice, sea level has risen again. This has caused the Sussex rivers to lose gradient and meander down their valleys and fill them with detritus. Longshore drift has also moved sand and gravel into protective coastal banks, notably where the softer shales met the sea at Pevensey Levels and south of Romney Marsh, allowing the reclamation of pastures and the reincorporation of islands in historic time.

The most recent surface erosion has further levelled the clay vales and modified the surface of the uplands. It has articulated the contrast between the sands and clays in the Wealden beds, giving the former an infertile gravelly surface interrupted by occasional low rectilinearly-fissured cliffs and causing the latter to form lower ground and carry the drainage. It has modified the chalk by expanding the dipslope valleys and the scarp-slope re-entrants and causing some solution of its surface, leaving behind residual spreads of clay-with-flints.

Introduction

We can best understand the geology of an area by looking at the surface appearance of the ground. There are three main types of indicator.

1. Exposures of rock at the surface called *outcrops* where the soil has been stripped away. These include cliffs, cuttings, and quarries.

2. The nature and shape of the landforms. Most rock types are associated with specific slope angles, valley forms, soils and plants. Chalk, shale, and sandstone give quite distinct surface forms.

3. Buildings, especially old churches, castles, and manor houses contain local stone. Rudyard Kipling's Batemans at Burwash, for example, used Ashdown Sandstone. Shelly limestone from Weald Clay was used for ornamental pieces such as baptismal fonts, including the one at Lurgashall, and as building stone called 'Sussex marble' or 'winkle stone' (because of its snail-like *Viviparus* shells) for churches. Flint and limestone can be found in most churches near the Downs, sometimes in chequer patterns as at Hiorn's Tower, Arundel Castle. Stiff limey clay ('clunch') and sandstone appear as materials in Washington Church.

The place of geology in scenery is best displayed along the coast, where cliffs of chalk, limestone and sandstone contrast markedly with the windswept expanses of recently deposited silts and clays which reach their widest development in Romney Marsh.

The only rock that shows enough fossils to find on an ordinary Sussex walk is the chalk. Fossils are relatively rare in all other deposits.

GEOLOGICAL TIME

The main series in chronological order from the bottom. Provisional dates have been given to these ages, generally assigning the commencement of the Palaeozoic period to about 560 million years ago, but there is increasing evidence that such dating is doubtful, and that the whole story could have happened in a much shorter time.

QUATERNARY
    Holocene – Recent
    Pleistocene – Ice Age

TERTIARY (CENOZOIC)
    Pliocene
    Miocene
    Oligocene
    Eocene

SECONDARY (MESOZOIC) Triassic
    Cretaceous
    Jurassic
    Triassic

PRIMARY (PALAEOZOIC)
    Permian
    Carboniferous
    Devonian
    Silurian
    Ordovician
    Cambrian

PROTEROZOIC

ARCHAEOZOIC

The Geological History of the Weald

The geological history of the weald is a story of the changing of the one vast primal continent into the complex picture we see today. This continent is called Pangaea. It was built of rocks now called *Archaeozoic* and *Proterozoic*. They experienced three vast incidents of upheaval and mountain building, called 'revolutions'. These were separated by periods of relative quiescence which allowed massive erosion of the mountains and the deposition of the resulting materials into vast thicknesses of sedimentary beds or *strata*. These strata contain the remains of living things in the form of fossils.

Each revolution uplifted and contorted all the previous strata. In Britain, the first such revolution is called 'Caledonian' and was followed by the deposition of the *Palaeozoic* or *Primary* rock strata. The second revolution is called *Armorican* and was followed by the deposition of the *Mesozoic* or *Secondary* strata. It seems that it was during this period that the main separation of the continent of Europe from Africa on the one hand, and from the Americas on the other, took place. The third revolution is called *Alpine* and was followed by the deposition of much of the *Cenozoic* or *Tertiary* strata, although most of the movements that affected Britain came after the commencement of this deposition. The final geological period is called *Quaternary*. It was not initiated by a revolution but by the last Ice Age, and it still continues today.

Each of these geological ages is subdivided into periods, as shown on the facing page, while the distribution of geological sediments in the Weald appears on pages 8–9.

MESOZOIC (SECONDARY)

From the point of view of surface form – those rocks exposed in the Weald – our geological history effectively begins in the Mesozoic period, the age of dinosaurs. Imagine a land lying to the north of Sussex while the county itself is an older platform gradually subsiding under the sea.

The elements weather this northern land and rivers wash its detritus on to the platform until it becomes very thick. At the bottom there are approximately 100 metres of Purbeckian (Jurassic) sediments. These appear in only three places in Sussex as inliers show through younger overlying rocks.

They occur in echelon form:
- Along the Dudwell valley about 5 miles west of Brightling with Ashdown beds to north and south (around 618219).
- In Darwell Wood and Limekiln Wood, where they are bounded by a fault to the north making it meet Wadhurst Clay (720196).
- In Archer Wood west of Battle (743185).

The beds reflect the changing circumstances of their deposition and consist of limestones, sandstones, and gypsum. Most contain some fossils. The limestone has oysters, bivalves (clam-like shells, also called lamellibranchs), gastropods and ostracods. The sandstones have blackened plants, fish and even iguanadons.

They have been of considerable commercial importance, providing one of the few sources of limestone in the central Weald. They were

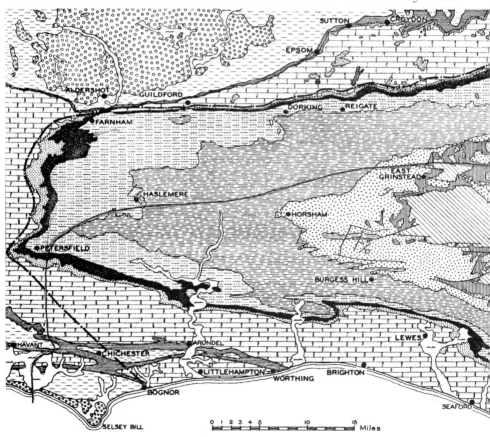

extensively excavated in the 18th and 19th centuries for agricultural lime and building stone. Even more important was the discovery in 1873 of extensive gypsum deposits lying just below the surface – the only commercially exploited gypsum deposits of Jurassic age in the United Kingdom. There are two mines, one at Mountfield (720194) and one near Brightling (677217), with a large industrial plant at the former. Because of the industry, the unspectacular terrain and general forest cover, it is not included as one of our walks. One of the better sections is along the river line just south-west of the Mountfield mines, where one can see a series of small exposures. However, access from the south is difficult because of lack of parking, and the entrance to the path is past a closed gate littered with debris. A visit to the gypsum mines themselves requires permission from British Gypsum at Robertsbridge.

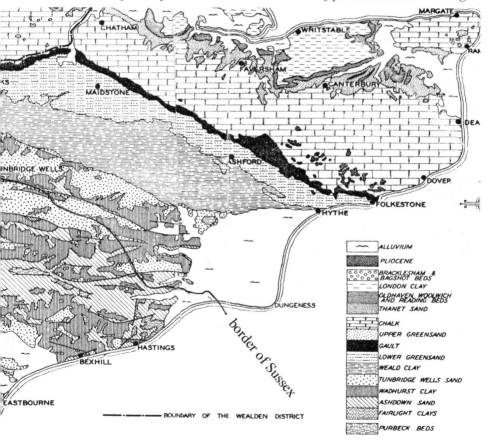

ALLUVIUM

PLIOCENE

BRACKLESHAM & BAGSHOT BEDS

LONDON CLAY

OLDHAVEN, WOOLWICH AND READING BEDS

THANET SAND

CHALK

UPPER GREENSAND

GAULT

LOWER GREENSAND

WEALD CLAY

TUNBRIDGE WELLS SAND

WADHURST CLAY

ASHDOWN SAND

FAIRLIGHT CLAYS

PURBECK BEDS

BOUNDARY OF THE WEALDEN DISTRICT

Above the Jurassic, Cretaceous sediments vary in thickness from about 1,800ft to 4,000ft (550–1,220m). After their deposition, the sea retreated and there was intense compression from the south. This buckled them into a long east-west dome resembling a pile of inverted dishes with the smallest at the bottom. This is called an *anticline*. The elements then got to work on this dome and unroofed the top so as to expose the raw edges of the beds forming it (*see page 73*).

These sediments differ from the Jurassic because the depositing water became much less saline, as evidenced by many fresh-water fossils. They show a rhythmic alternation of sand and mud, reflecting the changing mechanics of deposition. Flood waters deposit sand (particles generally 0.05–2mm in diameter) where the gradient is steep and the flow strong. Clay (particles smaller than 0.02mm) is deposited where water is impounded and still. Silt particles (0.002 and 0.05mm in diameter) reflect intermediate conditions. These textural variations in sediments enable us to infer the climatic changes and height changes in the source area of sediments around London.

The lower half of the Cretaceous sequence, called Wealden, is shown below, with the oldest deposits at the bottom.

The sands show few fossils but are rich in blackened plant fragments. The clays contain more fossils. The Fairlight Clays are well exposed on the cliffs east of Hastings but have few inland exposures. The few animal fossils include the casts of fresh water molluscs and insects. The plant fossils found there include a tree fern (*Tempskya schimperi*), ordinary ferns, a pine-like tree, cycads, and occasional lignite. The

---

WEALDEN SERIES (Cretaceous)
Approximate range of thickness

Weald Clay 400–1400ft (120–430m)
Upper Tunbridge Wells Sand up to 220ft (67m)
Grinstead Clay 25–75ft (8–23m)
Ardingly Sandstone 50ft (16m)
Lower Tunbridge Wells Sand 100–150ft (30–46m)
Wadhurst Clay 110–235ft (33–72m)
Ashdown Sands 650–750ft (200–230m)
Fairlight Clays 0–400ft (0–120m)

Ashdown Sands also have only a few fossils, but they are of the same types and notably include the freshwater molluscs *Unio and Neomiodon*.

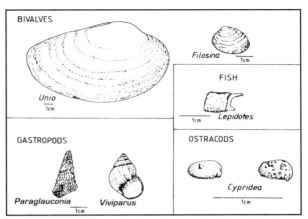

Fossils found in the Weald Clay.

The Wadhurst Clay contains sandstone beds rich in fossils, including dinosaurs (an iguanodon with footprints was found near Cuckfield), crocodiles, turtles, pterodactyls, and the horsetail plant *Equisetites lyelli*. It also contains ironstone nodules, especially towards the bottom, which gave rise to the Sussex iron industry.

There was a re-elevation of the source area around London after the deposition of the Wadhurst Clay. This increased the gradient of the inflowing water and began another cycle of deposition. In the Tunbridge Wells Sands, sandstones alternate with clays reflecting respectively the alternate raising and lowering the height difference between the source and receiving areas. Fossils are rare throughout these beds. The Lower Tunbridge Wells Sands is followed in turn by the Grinstead Clay, the Upper Tunbridge Wells Sands, the Ardingly Sandstone and then the Weald Clay.

The Ardingly Sandstone is a massive bed on top of the Lower Tunbridge Wells Sands which gives rocky outcrops. The Weald Clay is the thickest of the subdivisions of the Wealden Series. It was laid down on mudflats exposed at intervals. It contains limestone with fresh water snails, and 'marbles' containing invertebrate fossils (*Paludina*, lamellibranchs, occasional gastropods, including the fresh water gastropod *Viviparus*, and the near-marine brackish *Filosina*).

Fossil iguanodon footprint found on Bexhill Beach, probably on Tunbridge Wells Sands.

Greensands and Gault

Another subsidence of the area allowed an invasion of the sea from the south, converting the fresh water Wealden lake into a salt water bay, permitting the deposition of the Lower Greensand, the Gault Clay, and the Upper Greensand.

The Lower Greensand has its main outcrop on the northern side of the Weald where it forms a ridge locally higher than the Chalk, including Leith Hill, the highest point in south-east England. This is because it is capped by resistant chert bands.

The Gault is a stiff, inky blue clay supplied by erosion from Lower Greensand. It has a rich and varied fossil fauna, including many bivalves, cephalopods including ammonites, gastropods (snails), some echinoids (sea urchins), brachiopods ('lamp shells'), fish teeth, lobsters,

---

THE SUBDIVISIONS OF THE LOWER GREENSAND

4. Folkestone Beds 5–250ft (2–75m): sandstone with strong current bedding; fossils rare, chiefly lamellibranchs.

3. Sandgate Beds 30–115ft (9–35m): sandstone and limestone; fossils somewhat more common, including sea urchins, bivalved molluscs, gastropods and brachiopods.

2. Hythe Beds 0–350ft (0–100m): sandstone the main former of high ground, fossils rare and resemble those of the Atherfield Clay. It is capped by bands of chert (flint-like silica which differs from it usually in having browner colours and fracturing along flat rather than shell-shaped planes).

1. Atherfield Clay 0–65ft (0–20m): mainly in Kent and Surrey; disappears east of Lewes. It has a rich collection of marine fossils in contrast to the brackish and fresh water types in the Weald Clay. There is a sharp change from the underlying Wealden, becoming much more marine. The fossils found there include cephalopod molluscs such as ammonites and nautiloids, bivalved and univalved molluscs, brachiopods and reptiles of ichthyosaur and plesiosaur type. Vegetable fossils include pines, cycads and ferns. The land creatures include dinosaurs.

---

crabs, corals and driftwood. It forms the low ground between the Downs. Its best exposure, much disturbed and squeezed, is on the foreshore below Beachy head.

The Upper Greensand is similar to the Lower Greensand but thinner. Fossils are rare, but there are molluscs, especially bivalves, and animal burrows. It includes malmstone (a mixture of sand, clay, and chalk) with sponge spicules.

Chalk

The Chalk was deposited in a thick sheet over the area that is now south-eastern England and northern France. The sea, at an event called the 'Cenomanian Transgression', had submerged the whole area 400–2,000ft (120–600m) deep, the nearest land and source of materials probably being Wales. The deposit began as a muddy coccolith ooze, over 95 per cent calcium carbonate ($CaCO_3$). Coccoliths are secreted by foraminifera (microscopic planktonic algae), about 360 per millimetre.

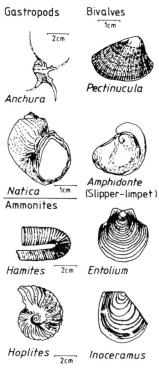

Fossils found in the Gault.

The Chalk also contains many shells, including lamellibranchs, brachiopods, marine reptiles, fishes, *Micraster* (sea urchins), ammonites, belemnites, nautiloids and other molluscs.

The fossils give a clue to the environment in which the creatures lived. They are of three types:

– floating (*planktonic*): mostly coccoliths of calcareous algae and foraminifera with their larvae

– free-swimming (*nectonic*): fish, sharks, swimming reptiles, ammonites, and belemnites

– bottom dwelling (*benthonic*): bivalves, echinoids, sponges and spicules, starfish (moved on the sea floor), together with some crustaceans and worms. Harder ground on the sea floor was occupied by corals and brachiopods who preferred the less muddy water and faster flow.

Flint is especially important because it is so widespread and the hardest tool-making material and building stone found in the whole of southeastern England. It can contain fossils, usually bivalves and micropscopic radiolaria (tiny lattice-like Protozoa with arrangements of rods and spines) whose remains have been replaced atom by atom with amorphous silica.

The origin of flint is debated. It is either due to silica segregation within the chalk at the time it was deposited or to later percolating water charged with carbon dioxide: this forms calcium bicarbonate

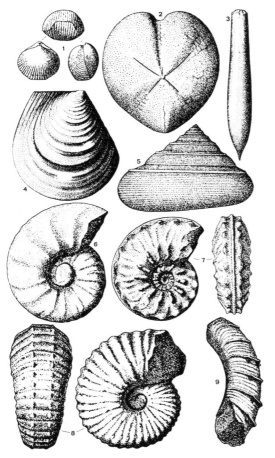

Common fossils of the chalk:

1 Brachiopod (Middle Chalk)

2 Echinoid (Upper Chalk)

3 Belemnite (Plenus Marls, top of the Lower Chalk)

4 Bivalve (Lower Chalk)

5 Gastropod (Gault, Upper Greensand and Chalk)

6–9 Ammonites
  (6 & 9 from Middle Chalk;
   7 & 8 from Lower Chalk)

whose removal leaves gaps for silica gel to accumulate and harden. Sometimes a lump of flint will contain a geode with attractive crystals.

When long exposed, flint often turns white. This is thought to be due to the carbon dioxide differentially removing the colloidal silica and leaving behind the less easily soluble quartz as fibres and grains which give it colour. Chert pebbles are also common everywhere. This is a coarser and less homogenous material of the same composition as flint that usually originates in limestone and is often brown because of iron coloration.

Also, throughout the chalk but particularly in the Lower Chalk, there are occasional crystals of iron pyrites. These are often cubical in form and yellow-brown in colour. They may somewhat resemble gold, justifying the name 'fool's gold'. They are always formed in place.

THE SUBDIVISIONS OF THE CHALK

The Upper Chalk is the thickest of the three and has many marine fossils and abundant flint. The top strata are composed of the 28m thick *Gonioteuthis quadrata* chalk, a goniatite (globular ammonite-like) fossil specific to this deposit. The dominant scarp former is the Chalk Rock which defines its lower limit.

The Middle Chalk begins at the bottom with the Melbourn Rock and has few flints. It is generally less fossiliferous but the fossil *Micraster* appears.

The Lower Chalk, visible at Beachy Head, is less pure and has more marl (calcareous clay with more than 15 per cent calcium carbonate), which decreases upwards. It has no flints. It is very fossiliferous, with many *ammonites* and bivalves including *brachiopods*, but rarely *gastropods, which are* mainly in the lowest beds. There are *echinoids* throughout, usually fragmented, and small *corals* are common. There are also *fish* teeth and the remains of marine reptiles *(Ichthyosaurus)*. Its top is characterised by 'plenus marl': this is because it contains the index fossil belemnite; *Actinocamax plenus.*

CENOZOIC (TERTIARY)

Uplift at the end of the Cretaceous gave a land surface sloping downwards towards the east. A major trunk river flowed along the line of the present Thames. Renewed pressure from the south throughout the Tertiary period caused the area to experience pulsed uplifts combined with folding. The Weald remained a land area and developed the major east-west fold pattern we see today.

At the same time it experienced continuous erosion. This began in the Eocene period and became intense in the Miocene period, so we do not find many surface deposits in Sussex. Nevertheless, there are local occurrences of two of the four main Eocene beds recognized in the London area, as shown below.

By the mid-Eocene erosion had breached the Chalk covering of the Wealden dome to reveal the Lower Greensand. There was little deposition in the Oligocene because the area was subjected to folding and elevation associated with the strong 'shove' from the south which also formed the Alps. Sussex experienced the 'outer ripples of the Alpine storm,' which gave the Weald and the London Basin their final folded form.

Erosion of the surface continued during the Miocene and Pliocene periods (collectively called Neogene), but did leave some Pliocene deposits containing fossils on Beachy Head and some barren ironstone and iron-bearing sandstone on the nearby Downs.

EOCENE DEPOSITS IN THE WEALD
in order of superposition

2. London Clay, seen in an outlier at Newhaven, Bognor, and Chichester. Fossils are rare except at Bognor where there are lamellibranchs, gastropods and sharks' teeth.

1. Woolwich, Oldhaven & Reading Beds. The Reading Beds are purple and grey mottled clays extending from Chichester to Worthing where they rest directly on Chalk. There are small outliers on South Downs near Brighton, Newhaven, and Seaford – about 100ft (30m) thick near Chichester. There is an exposure in a brickyard at Clapham near Worthing, and numerous exposures in the more sandy beds near Newhaven and Peacehaven.

Tertiary deposits are embedded in the coastal rock exposed in sections such as Black Rock at Brighton. The explanation of this section seems to draw on a combination of causes: the remains of material formerly overlying them, cryoturbation (churning and heaving due to freeze-thaw) and dissolution of the underlying chalk. We can also see Tertiary rocks around the village pond at Falmer, where they are incorporated into walls and buildings.

The end of the Tertiary period saw an almost total submergence of the area under the Pliocene 'Calabrian' sea. This left its traces from about 500–820ft (150–250m) by bevelling a beach surface on the Downs and parts of the High Weald. When this sea retreated, erosion revived and re-established the previous drainage pattern.

On the top of the Downs, and also in valleys and on beaches, we sometimes find dark red, almost black, ironstone pebbles. Some may be concretions from the Lower Greensand and Hastings Beds and some from Tertiary rocks later than the Chalk. On the surface of the Downs we can also find *sarsen* stones, e.g. at Stanmer Park. These are indurated sandstone boulders thought to be relics of the Tertiary beds which overlaid the chalk before their removal by erosion.

QUATERNARY

Pleistocene
The Pleistocene period is associated with the Ice Age that brought ice sheets to cover the whole of the British Isles north of the Thames. Its surface deposits are mainly loose materials moved locally by ice, wind or water, known collectively as *drift*. The many associated fossil plants and creatures are similar to those living today.

Sussex was influenced by glaciation but was not itself glaciated. Relics of the Ice Age are mainly seen in the traces of coastal terraces, in the steep slopes of the chalk thought to be due to erosion under the freezing conditions which made it less absorbent, and in some of the surface deposits indicating *periglacial* (ice-margin) conditions.

The sea rested at a number of levels between 690ft (210m) above and 100ft (30m) below present sea level. This left 'raised beaches' on the South Downs. The Calabrian sea was the highest and preceded the onset of the ice. There are also level areas bevelled and scoured by the sea at 393ft, 320ft, 196–220ft, 98ft and 25ft (120m, 98m, 60-67m, 30m and 7.5m), the last two being the best developed. All the raised and submerged beaches are thought to result from the oscillations of sea level coinciding with the freezing and melting of ice in the northern hemisphere. The falls in sea level occurred at times when the glaciers were most extensive. This 'tied up' much sea water in ice and therefore gave a relative elevation of the land. This elevation allowed the rivers, notably the Arun, to cut deep channels and intermittently to form flights of terraces of decreasing height. The interglacial, and especially

THE QUATERNARY SEQUENCE (inverse order of time)			
SYSTEM	PERIOD	WEALD	SOUTH COAST
Holocene	Flandrian Post glacial	Infilling of buried channels – flood plain development	
Upper Pleistocene	Devensian (Weichselian)	Arun terraces 1,2,3 & 4	Incision to form buried channels
	Ipswichian Interglacial		25ft (7.5m) 'Brighton Rock' raised beach
Middle Pleistocene	Wolstonian (Gippingham)	Arun terraces 5 &6	
	Hoxnian Interglacial		Goodwood-Slindon–Tortington 100ft (30m) raised beach
	Anglian	200ft (60m) platform	
	Cromerian		
	Beestonian		
	Pastonian		Higher levels on South Downs
		Unknown	
Lower Pleistocene	Baventian		
	Antian		
	Thurnian		
	Ludhamian		
	Waltonian		

the post-glacial, rises in sea level reduced these gradients and caused the same rivers to meander and to fill their valleys with alluvium.

The 25 foot (8m) raised beach is the most extensive and is thought to be Upper Pleistocene. It has a base at 10ft (3m) and a surface at 25ft (8m) above Ordnance Datum west of Brighton, especially at Portslade and Black Rock. It is locally developed across the basal 650ft (200m) of the Chalk succession as at Littlehampton, but it mainly developed across Eocene and Oligocene deposits. Its maximum width is 7½ miles (12km) near Chichester and it underlies most of the coastal plain west of Worthing. It is well preserved around Worthing and at Black Rock, where it is 29ft (9m) wide, but it disappears to the east of this. It is covered with *coombe deposits*. These are unsorted piles of postglacial sludge also called *head*. It is thought that the removal of the greater part of Highdown Hill (part of the Littlehampton fold of the Portsdown structure) was probably by the sea when it was at this level. It is visible along the coast road between Brighton and Worthing and is thought to form the level ground between Kingston Gorse (087015) and West Kingston Farm (080026).

The 100 foot (30m) raised beach is cut in the Chalk and preserved in part at Waterbeach, Slindon, Eartham, and Tortington, where one can see exposures. It is well preserved between Arundel and Havant, rising to 120ft (36m) at the inner edge near Chichester. The associated gravels are overlain by thick *loess* and *coombe rock*. Loess is wind-borne unstratified silt thought to have come from areas left by retreating ice. At Highdown Hill it laid down clays, sands and gravel. It is also visible in cliff sections such as Selsey Bill (8492) or in gravel pits such as around Chichester at (8703). It is well preserved at Arundel and rises to 120ft (36m) at its inner edge near Chichester, where the associated beach gravels are overlain by thick loess and coombe rock. The raised beaches are echoed by river terraces, notably in the Arun. Examples can be seen at the National Trust Slindon property (973075) and in the area between Boxgrove Common (915076), Eartham Thicket (924084) and Norton Lane (931075).

Evidence for the last low sea level can be seen in the Neolithic forest, now drowned, exposed at low tide at Cliff End, east of Hastings (895135).

The Pleistocene deposits in chronological order, starting with the oldest:

1. Plateau gravels, spread on higher ground. They have been left behind by the solution or erosion of softer surrounding material. They are sometimes called 'lag deposits' because their removal has lagged behind that of their surroundings. The most outstanding of these is *clay-with-flints* (e.g. at 336033). This deposit covers the Downs in many places to a depth of up to 50 feet (15m). There are three main theories of its origin, all of which may have some truth. It may be a) a relic of Tertiary strata which once overlaid the Chalk and have since been eroded away, b) a product of the weathering of the clay originally contained in the Reading Beds, the lowest of these strata or c) dissolution of the underlying chalk to leave its clay content behind, mixing with flints by cryoturbation.

2. Wealden Drift. This consists of coombe deposits on the South Downs. These are well exposed in cliff sections between Brighton and Eastbourne, especially at Blackrock and Birling Gap. The material is a mixture of loosened particles, ranging in size from stones to clay, which has drifted downslope in chalk valleys by a process known as *solifluction*. It rests at the bottom of chalk valleys and subsequently hardens into coombe rock. Coombe deposits sometimes rest on frost-shattered chalk. Some of the materials, e.g. at Black Rock, are from gravels of the 25ft (7.5m) raised beach which are now buried under 66ft (20m) of surface deposits.

3. *Brickearth*, so called because of its value in brick making. It is fine-textured wind-blown material which has been re-sorted and redeposited by water. It contains *loess*. Its origin is ascribed to wind transportation from the formerly exposed floor of the North Sea. This conclusion is based on the observation that these deposits become finer grained westwards. Brickearth lies mainly on the Sussex coastal plain and in the central Weald.   .

4. Widespread surface river and beach deposits overlying older rocks.

5. The submerged forests at Cliff End, Hastings and at Bexhill.

6. Numerous *erratics* on Sussex raised beaches, which suggest an ice sheet moving up the Channel.

7. River gravels, in which hand axes and fossil elephants and rhinos have been found.

8. Periglaciation is also seen in *cambering* where a moist clay layer becomes unfrozen, allowing it to become plastic and flow laterally under the weight of overlying rock.

Holocene (Recent)
Deposits from this period include alluvium at Romney Marsh and Pevensey filling in arms of the sea, shingle beaches and blown sand on Romney Marsh

DRAINAGE EVOLUTION

The rivers Arun, Adur, Ouse and Cuckmere originated as south-flowing streams off the Wealden dome during the early Tertiary. The summits of the chalk downs east of the Arun Gap formed a chain of islands at the time of the Calabrian sea. Their tributary strike streams run into the neighbouring rivers: the Rother into the Arun, and both the Bevern Stream and the branches of the Adur above Henfield (216163) into the Ouse.

The four main rivers now all cut through the South Downs and, because of their low gradients, have deposited silt and clay along their beds in such a way as to leave 'alluvial carpets' extending from the Weald down to the sea. All have meandered, forming S-shape curves within their valleys and undercutting their sides.

River capture is quite common in the Weald when two neighbouring streams each extend their headwaters by backward erosion. If one of the two streams is at a lower level, one of its tributaries will cut into the tributary of the other and capture it, robbing the second of a part of its catchment and diverting its flow into its own valley.

The Arun was an aggressive stream and captured tributaries of the Adur, Mole and Wey. The Cuckmere is now facing possible capture from streams draining into Pevensey haven. Both the Arun and the Ouse have widened their valleys over the Gault outcrop.

The Ouse's tributary, the Glynde, is a small stream with a small catchment, yet it occupies one of the largest gaps in the South Downs. It has lowered the Low Weald part of its basin more than have the major streams on each side. There are three theories which aim to explain this, and each may be a partial explanation. The first is that it was originally a continuation of the Uckfield branch of the Ouse; the second is that it occupies a former Ouse meander; and the third is that it developed as a stream following the soft rocks of the Palaeogene (Eocene and Oligocene series combined) filling of the Caburn syncline and of the weaker lower Cretaceous strata exposed by the unroofing of the Beddingham fold.

At times of glacial maximum the Thames/Rhine flowed down the Channel and there is evidence that the Sussex rivers joined it (the Ouse at Newhaven – 29.5m, Arun and Arundel – 33.5m). This created shingle structures along the sea shore which have since been moved by coastal currents. Groynes have accelerated coast erosion in their lee as at Seven Sisters.

The great final rise of sea level called the 'Flandrian Transgression' followed the Devensian glaciation (*see page 18*). The removal of the ice caused formerly heavily glaciated lands to rise in relation to the lightly glaciated or unglaciated areas to the south of them. Thus, northerly areas such as the highlands of Scotland are still rising while those around the southern North Sea and Channel are falling, causing a local rise in sea level currently estimated at about 2mm per year.

This rise has affected the Sussex rivers. They are tidal for some distance inland. Their mouths have suffered tidal scour. They have modified their earlier fluvial features by levelling them and undercutting their banks. This can be seen, for instance, along the lower Ouse as far inland as Glynde. They have become more sluggish and choked their valleys with alluvium, locally encouraging marshy conditions and the growth of bogs. When long established, these tend to grow upwards into *raised bogs*. At Amberley Wild Brooks there is a derelict raised bog on blue clay.

The Cuckmere, looking towards High and Over from Exceat.

Today's Wealden Scenery

Although varying in detail, each of the main geological belts has its own characteristic appearance. Much of the High Weald is heath covered, though parts are wooded and parts well cultivated. Good viewpoints are rare, but where visible they show scattered copses, small irregular arable fields, sheep pastures and the occasional regular patterning of orchards and hop gardens. The Lower Greensand is not very fertile, and is mainly heath-covered or wooded with coniferous trees. The low lying clay belts of the Gault Clay and the Weald Clay are heavily timbered and mainly agricultural. Chalk country has soft, rounded outlines and is grass-covered and bare of trees except where superficial deposits are present in some thickness.

The scenic variety is best displayed along the coast where cliff lines of chalk, limestone and sandstone contrast markedly with the windswept flat expanses of recently deposited alluvium which reach their widest development in Romney Marsh.

Wealden Beds

Lying above the Purbeck Beds are the Hastings Beds and Weald Clay, known together at Wealden. They outcrop across the central Weald in a wide band from Haslemere to Hastings. The Hastings Beds occur in the centre of an area surrounded by a long horseshoe of Weald Clay.

The folds in the Weald reflect the flexures in the deep-seated underlying rocks called 'Basement Complex' with the higher ground over its upfaulted parts. The Crowborough, Battle and Hastings folds give the major ridges, which are due to folding as a result of subsurface pressure on the Weald from the south. Crests decline in height eastwards.

The main outcrops of the Ashdown Sands are in Ashdown Forest and between Uckfield and Winchelsea. There is also a good exposure in the coast section at Galley Hill, Bexhill, and in several large excavations inland, such as a quarry about a mile south of Hartfield and a second one near Fairlight church, where white and almost pure quartzose sand has been dug.

The Hastings Beds are hilly and wooded with fine views over deeply winding valleys dissecting the high sandy plateau. However, drainage is sometimes bad because of the fineness of the sandstone and the

The main geomorphological areas of Sussex:

Q   *Recent alluvium*

i 4–7   *Barton, Bracklesham and Bagshot Beds (sandy and gravelly)*

i 1–3   *Sandy beds and London Clay*

h 5   *Chalk*

h 3–4   *Gault Clay etc*

h 2   *Lower Greensand etc*

h 1   *Weald Clay*

h   *Hastings (sandstone) Beds*

g 14   *Purbeck Beds*

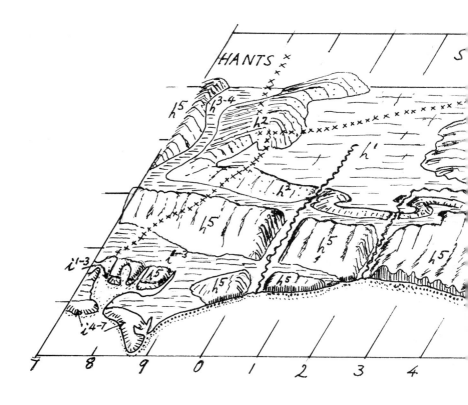

presence of clay bands, except for Ashdown Forest on the Ashdown Beds. The best exposures are of the Ardingly sandstone, which is the top of the Lower Tunbridge Wells sandstones, are at:

Chiddinglye Wood & Philpots quarry at West Hoathly, four miles south-west of East Grinstead, where there is a view from the church to the South Downs.

Stone Hill rocks, two miles south of East Grinstead, near Weir Wood Reservoir.

Harrison's Rocks, about a mile south of Groombridge, by the railway.

Eridge Rocks, at Eridge Green, two miles south-west of Tunbridge Wells.

Bowle's Rocks, two miles north-east of Crowborough

Tunbridge Wells High Rocks and Toad Rock

Rocks Wood in Rocks Park, Uckfield.

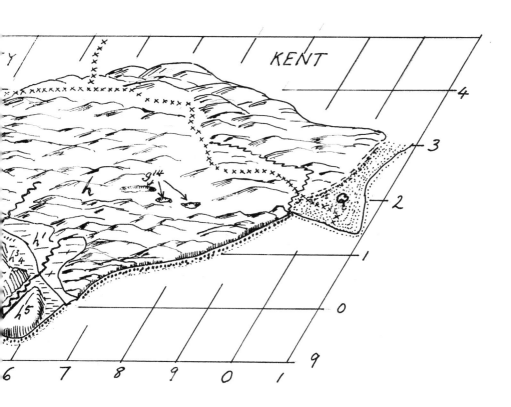

The Lower Greensand *cuesta* is largely due to the resistance of the Hythe beds.

The Gault Clay, Weald Clay, and Wadhurst Clay form the lowest ground and their weakness allows the greatest indentation along the coast. Inland they are well wooded and usually in pasture. There is a good section near Battle and on cliffs near Hastings and Cooden. The Weald Clay contains lenses of 'Paludina marble', also sometimes called Sussex marble, Petworth marble or Bethersden marble, which will take a polish and has been used in building. The Tilgate Stone is a hard calciferous (lime-rich) sandstone within the Wadhurst Clay. It is worked at Crowhurst, near Bexhill, where it is overlaid by a thin bed of conglomerate where numerous dinosaur bones have been found. There are no inland exposures of the Gault in Sussex, and the coastal ones are obscured by other materials.

The Chalk Lands

The South Downs coincide almost exactly with the Middle and Upper Chalk and the latter forms the tops. The summits fall slightly in height from west to east: Butser Hill is the highest at 902ft (275m), then Beacon Hill 794ft (242m), Chanctonbury Ring 781ft (238m), Ditchling Beacon 745ft (227m) and Firle Beacon 712ft (217m). The variety of landscape is due to differences in structure, superficial cover and degree of dissection of the chalk. The dominant scarp former is the Chalk Rock near the bottom of the Upper Chalk. The Melbourn Rock at the base of the Middle Chalk makes minor promontories on the face of the South Downs. The north-facing scarp slopes are steepened by being less exposed to weathering and having remained longer frozen. The western area is more broken, and around Harting there are deep valleys completely breaching the chalk wall, e.g. between Harting Downs and Beacon Hill (807184). Cocking Gap (875155) possibly once crossed the chalk before being captured. The main dipslope valleys (valleys down the cuesta in the direction of dip of the strata) are characteristically flat-floored, steep sided and dry. There are some *dolines* on the surface due to differential solution of the chalk.

Above the Chalk Rock in the highest parts of the sequence there is a zone 92 ft (28m) thick containing a fossil goniatite (*Gonioteuthis quadrata*). This caps a discontinuous low escarpment several kilometres south of the main scarp crest. This material is called the 'quadrata chalk' and forms a broken secondary escarpment behind the main chalk escarpment. It has the form of north-facing prow-shaped hills or 'flatirons' separated by dipslope valleys. It can be traced all the way to Wiltshire where it rises to a maximum height at Sidbury Hill on Salisbury Plain. On the South Downs it is best developed around Blackpatch Hill and Cissbury Hill (*see below*). Its preservation is thought to be due to its increased permeability resulting from an effective joint pattern and numerous seams of nodular flints. It may also owe something to differential protection of the chalk under a variable cover of clay-with-flints.

In fact, the Chalk is not a single *cuesta* with uniform dip. It has locally experienced folding to create a series of synclines and anticlines. The Ouse crosses them all. Erosion has unroofed these folds and created the Vale of the Brooks immediately south of Lewes, surrounded by inward-facing chalk scarps. Mount Caburn marks the northern rim and Itford Hill (440055) the southern. The effect of these folds is to cause a) an embayment at the entrance to the Adur gap, and b) a peninsula of Lower Greensand extending west-northwest through Henfield. There is also a syncline at Newhaven, crossed by the Ouse, plunging (with axis descending) to the west. The Chyngton Gap east of Seaford shows it denuded of its Tertiary infilling, but outliers (isolated outcrops of younger rocks over older) of this filling survive at Newhaven and Seaford.

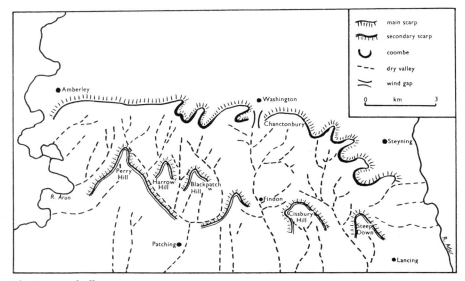

The Sussex chalk.

SURFACE FEATURES OF THE CHALK

Transverse valleys

The interruptions of the Chalk ridge are the valleys which cross it transversely in a general north-south direction. Surface streams probably excavated them. Chalk normally absorbs water, but streams can flow over it when held up by an impermeable or frozen bed which makes the chalk act as a rock rather than a sponge. There are three types of such valley on the Downs: the major 'windgaps' which traverse the whole chalk ridge, the *coombes* on the scarp face and the dipslope valleys.

1. Major *windgaps*. Four major rivers breach the crestline of the South Downs: the Arun, Adur, Ouse and Cuckmere. Between most pairs is a major wind gap: Cocking west of the Arun, Washington between Arun and Adur, Pyecombe between Adur and Ouse, and Jevington between Cuckmere and Eastbourne. But these gaps are not due to wind. They are thought to be the major dipslope streams which were 'captured' by others which expanded by dissolving the underlying chalk and receiving stronger flows of meltwater from retreating glaciers. The Arun has been aggressive against the Adur, Mole and Wey. Sometimes two valleys join

Devil's Dyke, near Brighton.

by headward erosion, such as Jevington Bottom in the area of Filching Manor, but such situations are rare.

2. Scarp-face coombes. These include:

a) shallow runnels fretting the scarp face,

b) small armchair-shaped or larger amphitheatre-shape coombes. These are especially visible where they break an abrupt edge as between Eastbourne and the Pevensey Levels. Meads Hollow (6098, now built up) has this form. The simplest are due to spring action and undersapping. Where the scarps are high, straight and steep, the coombes tend to be short, straight, and simple with gently inclined floors and with sides of over 30° on bare chalk and terminating in a steep headwall. They therefore have a U-shaped cross section in formerly glaciated areas, which can be exaggerated by ploughing the valley floor. The slopes are usually bare chalk. Hollows are filled with coombe rock.

c) more angular penetrations up to several miles long, usually fault-guided and at right angles to the local escarpment trend. Examples are the Devil's Dyke near Brighton (facing page), Sullington (096120, near Storrington), Fulking (245103, near Brighton) and Folkington Bottom (555035, near Wilmington).

3. Dipslope valleys towards the Channel with well-developed branching networks. They began when the land was at high level after the retreat of the Calabrian sea. They can be straight, arcuate, meandering or zigzag. They are often related to the joint system, as in the dry valleys around Brighton and Butser Hill. Bostal Bottom (490047), Blackstone Bottom (490030) and Charleston Bottom (535002) also illustrate this very strongly. There was relatively little periglacial erosion during the Ice Age on north-facing slopes because they would remain frozen.

By contrast the slopes facing south and south-west thawed out more readily and experienced more weathering and solifluxion, allowing masses of lubricated sludge to move downhill towards the valley bottom over the still frozen subsurface. As a result these slopes are much steeper, as we can see, for instance, looking north from Cradle Hill just north-west of High and Over (510012). The upper reaches of such valleys are steep with impressive headwalls. Other examples are at Long Furlong, Worthing (105077), Blackstone Bottom, Seaford (489031) and Deep Dean, Lullington (539025). The valleys are now dry because the water table has dropped below their floors since glacial time.

Coast scenery

The reason the Sussex coast does not show the indentations one would have expected to develop along the exposed rock sequence is that the high coastline created by the Hastings Beds is flanked by two important areas of deposition of river-borne material which conceal former inlets cutting into the Weald Clay (*see below*). These are Dungeness in the east and Pevensey Levels in the west. The relatively short coast (17km) on the central Weald is on resistant Ashdown Sands. In the past this formed a headland which sheltered the bay to the northeast. It gave sediments which accumulated in that direction and masked the old cliffed shoreline still discernible around the inland limits of Romney Marsh.

Some traces of higher raised beaches are occasionally visible on the South Downs above those at 98ft (30m) and 25ft (7.5m). They appear as horizontal 'bevels' across the chalk at heights of 393ft (120m), 308ft (94m) and 197–220ft (60–67m) above sea level.

Eroding coasts today

The Hastings Beds between Bexhill and Fairlight show walls of sandstone with an untidy apron of talus, sticky clay and boulders of sandstone. Waterfalls occur where coast erosion is more rapid than river downcutting. The Ashdown Sands give discontinuous steps and ledges, the lower parts of the cliff being concealed beneath fan-shaped deposits of outwashed material called *alluvial fans*, and of slopes on rockfall debris, including enormous sandstone blocks.

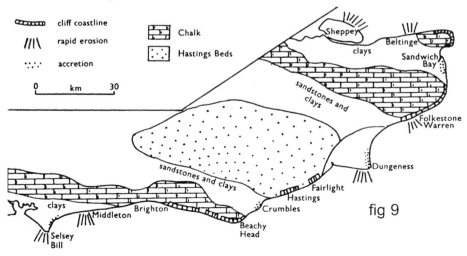

fig 9

The chalk cliffs westwards from Eastbourne run parallel to the strike and are the highest in southeastern England. The chalk resists wave attack less well than it does surface erosion because it cannot absorb the sea water. The cliffs are mostly on the Upper Chalk, clean cut and vertical above the wavecut platform. The feet are debris-free except for

Birling Gap: chalk cliff above wave-cut bench with flint bed over chalk.

flints and some rockfall debris. The retreat of the cliffs leaves 'hanging valleys' such as those that separate the Seven Sisters. At Birling Gap the cliff retreated 3ft (91cm) per year between 1875 and 1961, and the wave-cut bench is locally covered by a flint bed (*above*). Shore platforms cut across all deposits. At Brighton they suffer bio-erosion from mollusc borings.

The Sussex plain west of Bognor and Selsey Bill is on soft London Clay and later Tertiary deposits. These give a landscape of low relief with minor watercourses called 'rifes'.

Depositional coasts

The Flandrian rise in sea level has caused the sea to move much detritus caused at that time. Some has been deposited in *spits*. A double spit flanks Chichester harbour. This doubling is due either to a breaching of an earlier continuous spit or growth from opposite shores due to locally reversed drifting. The spit across Pagham Harbour is due to eastwards drift of material from Selsey Bill. It has sometimes been breached near its centre, but outward growth has since nearly closed it. Maps show that the coastal spit on which Shoreham stands grew 3½ miles (5.6km) between 1587 and 1783, but since then this has been arrested by the construction of groynes. The Ouse at Seaford has a spit, but natural breaching in combination with harbour works caused the exit to be stabilized on the west side near Newhaven, allowing it to become the main port.

Some coastal deposition enclosed two large marshes:

a) Langney Point.

The Pevensey and Willingdon Levels were a marshy and shallow bay in Roman times. A shingle bank spread north-eastwards along the coast between 1576 and 1736, enclosing and protecting them, allowing them to be almost wholly reclaimed by the beginning of the 18th century. The shingle has extended northwards since that time.

b) Dungeness.

Although mainly in Kent, it is relevant to consider Dungeness in a study of Sussex because of their linked geological origins. The Dungeness peninsula, including the reclaimed areas of Romney and Walland Marshes, is the greatest spread of shingle in the British Isles. It is larger than the Pevensey levels because the Hastings Beds provide less protection from coastal erosion than does the chalk at Eastbourne. Unfortunately the building of the power station and the many bungalows spoil much of the natural beauty of the area.

Its inland limit is a cliff line originally cut by the sea in the Flandrian period but absent in the Pevensey area. It runs from Cliff End, just east of Hastings, around the former Isle of Oxney to just east of Hythe, but it is broken by gaps made by the Rother, Tillingham and Brede. The cliffs are most pronounced at and near Winchelsea and Rye and east and west of Stutfall Castle, but all have much degraded through subaerial erosion since the retreat of the sea.

The outer shingle foreland of Dungeness is due to wave action representing a junction of up-Channel and down-Channel drift directions. It began with longshore ridges being built out eastwards from Fairlight Head in Palaeolithic times when that headland was about a mile further out to sea than today. This impounded marshes behind it. Then about 3,000 BC the land rose about 8 metres relative to the sea and forest started growing on the exposed sea floor. Some traces of this forest can still be seen on the beach near Hastings as fragments of silicified wood and in a peat layer in the soil.

In Romney Marsh today 100 feet (30 metres) of alluvial sediments overlie Hastings Beds and Weald Clay. The Rother has cut a broad valley across the area. This probably began in the Devensian period of the Ice Age and entered the sea at Hythe. Since then it has had its outfall diverted several times. It had probably left its northern course some time before Roman times.

The sea returned in Roman times, drowning the forests and causing the peat to be dissected by tidal channels. The incoming sea also breached the extended spits, which had become a bar, in two places, allowing the Rother to debouch near the present site of New Romney and the Tillingham and Brede to debouch to seaward of Winchelsea. More peat and clay were then deposited on top of the leaf mould and wood of the former forest bed.

From about the early ninth century the gradual fall of sea level allowed what is now Romney Marsh to emerge. The first areas to be reclaimed were naturally the highest parts. The process was piecemeal, each landowner taking in small areas when they were ready. The building of the Rhee Wall, first mentioned in a document in 1258, speeded the reclamation process (*see below*). The wall is really a great causeway running from Snargate to New Romney and is still a permanent feature, being followed by the B2080 (Snargate to Brenzett) and the A259 (Brenzett to New Romney). It was originally built as an artificial

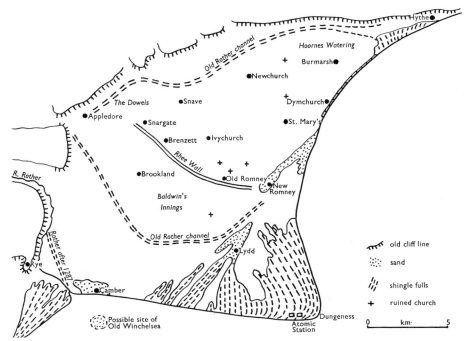

The Rhee Wall (centre of diagram) was built across Romney Marsh to keep the sea at bay

watercourse to bring the upland waters of the river Rother across to New Romney where they would help scour the rapidly silting harbour. The name 'wall' derives from its being between two artificial banks well above the surrounding marsh level.

But the Rother again moved south-west, and in 1287 it was diverted to Rye, near its present outfall, which is also that of the rivers Brede and Tillingham, into which it was artificially led in the 17th century. The continuing sedimentation allowed the marshes to be wholly reclaimed by this time.

The Rother's breach of the coastal bar at Winchelsea prevented the latter's continued extension to seaward. This breach starved the shore further east of shingle and allowed the large southerly waves to drive back the free inner end and cause the bend which was to develop into the highly angular form we see today. Once a slight bend was formed it tended to be self-propagating.

The forces which mould it today are threefold. Up-Channel waves cause the longshore drift. Round the Ness, however, the waves are reduced in size and swing around to a more northerly direction. But the throwing of the material into ridges is not the work of these oblique and much weakened up-Channel waves, but of the far larger northeasterly waves coming down-Channel from the North Sea. The sharpness of the Ness is due to the fact that no large waves reach it from a southeasterly direction where the French coast is nearest. Since 1300 the sea level in southeastern England has risen by about 5ft(1.5m). The result of this in Romney Marsh is to make the later and more easterly ridges somewhat higher than the westerly.

Thus great masses of shingle have extended across what was once a large bay and then silted up to form Romney Marsh. It has gradually been reclaimed in stages shown south of the Rhee Wall in the diagram on page 33.

Human Effects on the Landscape

In ancient times the Downs were the most intensively occupied region of southern Britain. The settlements tended to be on promontories and south-facing slopes. Besides Palaeolithic and Neolithic remains, prehistoric Celtic fields, probably of the early Iron Age, have been located at many places on the Sussex Downs. It was the Anglo-Saxons who moved down into the valleys.

The main evidence from the Stone Age is in the long barrows, e.g. at Alfriston. There are three between Jevington and Cuckmere, out of twelve for the whole South Downs. All were burial mounds for chiefs built 2,500–1,800BC in conspicuous positions. Flint was the basis of tools. African-style hut holes and many indicators of military defence have been found on the northern crest of Windover Hill and at Cissbury.

In the Bronze Age (generally 1,800–500BC): the Celts can be identified from round barrows, usually called tumuli on maps (e.g. Alfriston), and strip lynchets.

Iron Age (post-500BC) people still favoured the chalk uplands for causewayed camps, such as Coombe Hill, which is surrounded by two concentric banks close to the crest. The Romans brought roads, such as that running Fishbourne–Chichester–Stane Street–Pevensey (*below*). They

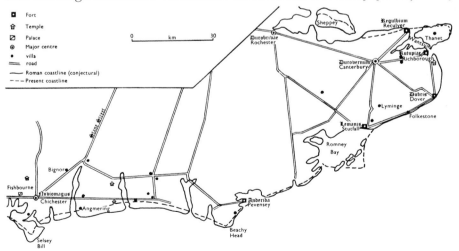

The Roman road from Fishbourne to Pevensey.

also put in rectilinear field and road layouts, called centuriation, as are still visible around Ripe, Chavington and Bignor, where there is a Roman villa.

In medieval times the Anglo-Saxons took the best land and gave us most of today's names, the Celtic place-names disappearing. Those ending in -ing indicate the settlement of so-and-so's people (Worthing, Brightling, Fulking, Patching). The suffix -ham means home or enclosure (e.g. Ickham, Wingham, Barham, and Elham), while -hurst means copse or wood (e.g. Wadhurst, Ticehurst, Salehurst). Their churches used a variety of local stones, as exemplified in Slaugham church with its carved stone monuments and Purbeck Marble font. The Anglo-Saxons also started an iron industry. This required the development of 'hammer ponds' held up by beds of impermeable clay, often in bead-like 'strings'. It gave rise to place names such as 'hammer', 'forge', 'furnace', 'pit', 'mine' and 'col' (charcoal). A hammer pond can be seen near Ardingly reservoir.

Today gypsum is still mined near Mountfield and Brightling using an aerial ropeway to transport material to Robertsbridge. Clay is mined from the Gault in southern Sussex for use with chalk in cement manufacture. Numerous brickworks extract Weald Clay, such as that at Southwater. The coastal towns developed on sandstones, and the Folkestone Beds are quarried as a source of building sands. The Upper Chalk is used for cement with a big quarry at Lewes.

On the ridgetop of the high dry downs you occasionally find shallow saucer-like depressions holding ponds above a layer of puddled clay, chalk or concrete. The purpose of these 'dewponds' was to provide drinking water for sheep. There were literally thousands of them between Beachy Head and Winchester in the heyday of downland sheep farming, before the invention of plastic water piping. The majority were lined with clay, to which quicklime was added to stop worm damage. Some had straw mixed with clay to reduce cracking in summer. Others had a layer of flints to prevent penetration by animals feet.

Despite their name, almost all of their water has always come from rainfall. Dew adds a very small amount, and clouds and mist reduce evaporation, especially in summer. Because they are fairly wide they have a large collecting area in relation to the actual water surface. Today, the few that still function, such as those on Lullington Heath and Kingston Hill, have been restored by conservationists.

The Walks

BE PREPARED

Under cliffs and in quarries it is important to wear hard hats and stout footwear. One should avoid damaging rock exposures: it is best where possible to concentrate on fallen debris ('talus') and look there for samples. Along the coast it is vital to beware of the tide, as there are risks in being cut off under cliffs. It is helpful to take a tool such as a knife or geological hammer and a hand lens.

The walks in this book are all on land to which there is public access. Where possible we follow marked footpaths, using especially those on National Trust and Forestry Commission properties and the South Downs Way. To visit surrounding private lands it is necessary to obtain permission, ideally by writing to the owner and including a stamped addressed envelope for reply. It is occasionally necessary to pay for parking.

The Ordnance Survey Explorer series maps at a scale of 1:25,000 are strongly recommended. For wider geological information it is also useful to have the relevant geological maps. The most useful series is at 1:50,000, and sheets can be purchased from the British Geological Survey sales offices in Nottingham and Edinburgh, and at the Natural History Museum in London.

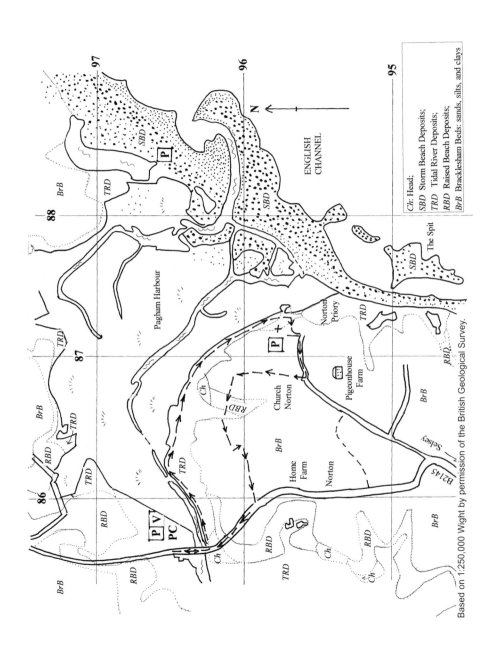

Based on 1:250,000 Wight by permission of the British Geological Survey.

Ch: Head;
SBD Storm Beach Deposits;
TRD Tidal River Deposits;
RBD Raised Beach Deposits;
BrB Bracklesham Beds: sands, silts, and clays

1. PAGHAM HARBOUR

OS 855922. Explorer map 120. Geological map: Wight sheet
50N 02W (1:250,000). 2 miles.
Visit the Selsey Visitor Centre at 858965 for any information
wanted on the area. Otherwise go direct to park at the old
church, Church Norton (872957).

The area around Selsey was the nucleus of the kingdom of the South
Saxons, hence the name Sussex. It seems likely that the first Saxon
king of Sussex, named Aella, first landed in 477 AD near Selsey, which
then stood further out to sea than today. The most likely place seems to
be the creek, called the Owers (873942). Selsey remained the nucleus
for the four centuries before the Norman Conquest. St Wilfrid, who landed
here in 681 from Northumbria, built a monastery and cathedral. Both
disappeared under the waves, which led to the removal of the see to
Chichester in 1091. It is believed that the lane past Grange Farm
(868949) once ran seaward to the cathedral and the site of old Selsey.
Place names in medieval documents indicate that villages between
Selsey Bill and Inner Owers sands have also been lost to the sea. It has
been suggested that the offshore area, still known as the Park,
represents the site of a former deer park for the bishops of Chichester
which existed as late as Tudor times.

South of a line east–west through Pagham Harbour the underlying
material is the sandy Bracklesham Beds. North of this almost up to
Chichester and extending west to Southampton it is soft London Clay.
This, where exposed to the sea, has been more easily eroded. Where the
sea has breached the Bracklesham Beds, as in Chichester and Langstone
harbours, it has widely extended its erosion of the soft clays behind. The
beach all around the Bill, but especially westward towards West
Wittering, is a rich hunting ground for the fossil fauna and flora of the
Bracklesham Beds, and also for Roman and pre-Roman coins and other
ancient artifacts.,

The cliffs at Selsey have been retreating since Saxon times. From
1875 this retreat has been by up to 26ft (8m) per year, though more
typically 7–20ft (2–6m). Surprisingly, more has gone from the southern
half of the east side of the Bill than from the more exposed west side,

whose north-west half is even advancing slowly through siltation. The reason for this greater retreat of the east side seems to be that the west side is to some extent protected by the gently sloping nature of the beach and the presence of an offshore reef of limestone called the Mixon. This was quarried and used in Selsey in the past, as can be seen in the walls of some older cottages in the town. By contrast, the upper part of the east beach is steeper and narrower and deepens rapidly offshore. The waves can thus attack more easily before they have lost much of their erosive power. The west beach is now protected by a concrete wall and the whole coast by wooden groynes. Since 1953 effective coast protection works and groynes have arrested serious erosion. The shingle behind groynes indicates the direction of longshore drifting. Along the East Beach it is from the Bill towards Pagham Harbour, feeding the sand spit which almost encloses it.

The chief Roman road of the peninsula ran from Chichester to Selsey. A Saxon charter mentions it as paved. Today it may be traced as a footpath across Donnington parish (854021), lying 450 yards east of the present road, the B2201. The lane and footpath leading north from Sidlesham crossroads (854992) between Street End and Brinfast Farm probably follows the same line. Beyond this the road from Church Norton (868955) to Selsey probably follows the line of the Roman original. The straight north-north-east/south-south-west part of the Birdham (819995) to Bracklesham (813964) road was probably also Roman.

THE WALK

From the car park at 858965 walk south for 200 yards down the road to a channel crossed by a bridge. This channel links the meandering channels known as the Broad Rife which are floored by tidal river deposits. This small river, whose meander curves survive between Birdham and Bracklesham, was cut by an advance of the sea west of Selsey. These curves can be clearly traced on Ordnance Survey Explorer Map 120.

Cross the bridge. At the sharp bend by Ferry House on the right is the end of a raised beach deposit which runs south. This beach is dated to the Ipswichian period, the last Interglacial period between the final Wolstonian and Devensian cold stages. Sea level was then higher than today because less water was held in permanent ice caps.

Turn immediately left on to the footpath along the raised bank enclosing the extensive salt marsh of Pagham Harbour.

View across the shingle at Pagham Harbour.

Note the system of channels in the harbour. The curve of the main harbour channel continues that of this shrunken river remnant The channels in the harbour reduce rapidly in size as they come inland from the sea because of the rapid dispersion of incoming tidal flow It is this rapid diminution of the size of channels inland that unmistakably differentiates sea channels from river channels. This distinction is useful in determining the origin of ancient channels. Former marine channels are called tidal palaeomorphs.

The shingle bank enclosing Pagham harbour is due to longshore drift from Selsey. The shingle comes from gravel beds capping the low cliffs around Selsey Bill. Other materials come from the offshore area known as the Park. Wave action sometimes brings this onshore, especially in the summer, although it is combed back outwards by the storms of winter. By the mid-17th century the embankment ran across the harbour, leaving only a narrow entrance to the north. After 1785 the spit began to extend north-east and by 1843 it had lengthened by 600 yards (550m). This growth forced the entrance channel of the harbour to cut deeply into the low clay cliff close to Pagham church. In 1876 the harbour was artificially sealed to counter this, the old entrance channel being left as a lake called Pagham Lagoon (883970). Attempts were then made to reclaim the mudflats of the former harbour, and many saltings were changed to pasture. The shingle barrier remained unbroken until 1910, when a south-east gale breached it, leaving two spits of almost equal length as in the 16th century. In the last 90 years the situation has remained like this, but the breach in the spit has moved northwards.

For a short distance to the west of the Bill the drifting is also to the east. West of the neighbourhood of Hillfield Road (850924), however, there is a drift parting, so that along most of the West Beach the movement of shingle along the upper beach is towards Bracklesham and the entrance to Chichester Harbour. There is some complexity in the area of parting, since there is often a different movement between the shingle on the upper beach, moving east, and the sand on the lower

St Wilfrid's chapel at Church Norton.

beach moving west. This may reflect the fact that the waves are moving the shingle while the longshore currents are moving the sand.

The survival of the Bill on soft rock facing waves blown by dominant winds is surprising. It is mainly due to two factors: the gentle gradient of the sea floor which reduces the force of attacking waves, and the existence of reefs, shoals or shallows which girdle the Bill about $4\frac{1}{2}$ miles from the shore. Many of these were above sea level in the Iron Age and Anglo-Saxon periods.

Pagham Harbour, previously known as Udring Haven, may owe its existence to drowning. There is a record of five square miles (1300 hectares) having been inundated about 1320. It became a flourishing sea port from which ships and men set sail for Agincourt and later to combat the Spanish Armada. The harbour was barraged in 1876 and the whole area reclaimed for agriculture, but the sea defences were destroyed in 1910, causing it to revert to saltmarsh and mudflat. Winter visitors include pintail, teal and brent geese. Summer visitors include shelduck, nesting terns, ringed plovers and oystercatchers.

After about 1 mile note the remains of St Wilfrid's chapel, the 13th century chancel of a church demolished in 1864 to provide material for the present church at Selsey. The nearby earthwork (872958) has provided the best available evidence for Iron Age settlement in the area. Its excavation revealed pottery and animal bones giving evidence of Iron Age, Roman and medieval occupation.

Continue south about 300 yards to visit the beach, and return the same way to the chapel. Note the beach materials – almost entirely flint, with occasional oyster shells. Note the effectiveness of this embanked gravel at resisting coast erosion.

Just south of the chapel, walk west past a car park and continue about 300 yards along the lane to Church Norton. Turn right along the path and follow it northwards. After about 500 yards it turns sharp left, but then generally parallels the walk beside Pagham Harbour. Turn right on the B2145 road and return to the car park.

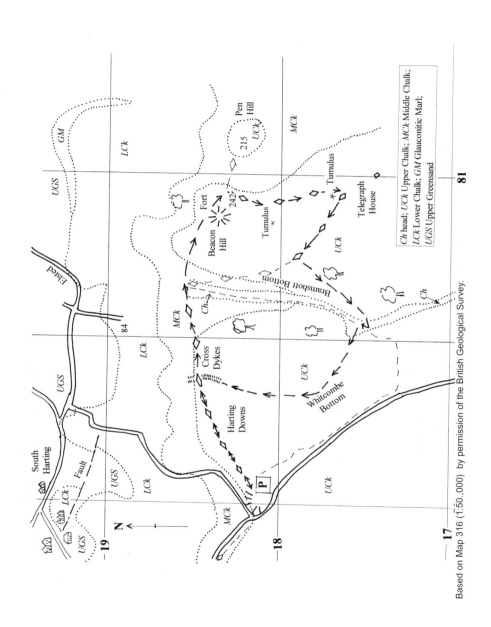

Based on Map 316 (1:50,000) by permission of the British Geological Survey.

Ch head; *UCk* Upper Chalk; *MCk* Middle Chalk; *LCk* Lower Chalk; *GM* Glauconitic Marl; *UGS* Upper Greensand

2. BEACON HILL

OS 807184. Explorer map 120. Geological Map: 316 Fareham Sheet (1:50,000). 2½ or 4 miles.

This is a classic South Downs walk. Start at the parking place at 790182 in the Harting Downs National Trust property.

THE WALK

Follow the South Downs Way eastwards along the top of the escarpment. After 700 yards note the cross dykes. After a further 500 yards the path drops steeply down in to a dip where an oak way post is embedded in a flint base. Note how closely the south-draining valley of Bramshott Bottom approaches the escarpment, a strategic location used by an earthwork and a near approach to the formation of a wind gap (an eroded lower place in the line of the escarpment). The valley bottoms

Looking west over South Harting from Harting Hill.

near the escarpment cut down into the Middle Chalk but the tops are on Upper Chalk.

From here follow the path up to the top of Beacon Hill with its Iron Age fort. At 795ft (242m), this is the fifth highest point on the Sussex Downs (after Littleton Down north of Bognor (837ft; 255m), Linch Hill (847175) (814ft; 248m), Ditchling Beacon (810ft; 247m) and Cross Dyke near Bignor (966132) (803ft; 245m). (Butser Hill in Hants (717203) is higher at 886ft (270m). This gives a view of some landforms. Under our feet are chalk and many flints.

The view from the trig pillar is grand and is assisted by a direction 'rose' nearby. Starting from Butser Hill and the hangers near Selborne in the west, we see north across the Rother valley to the extensive Lower Greensand hills, culminating in Leith Hill. Beyond these we can see north-east to the North Downs and east along the line of the South Downs, on a clear day to Ditchling Beacon 30 miles away and south to the east end of the Isle of Wight.

Nearer at hand to the north we see the inner ridges of the Weald. At our feet is the escarpment with the parallel larger re-entrants, middle sized hangers and small frets in the chalk scarp. On its face we can see the sequence from Upper Chalk down to Lower Chalk, the village of South Harting standing on the last. Its location is due to springs along the contact of the Chalk with the underlying Gault clay, which undercut and erode their back walls. Beyond the Gault clay vale the town of Midhurst to the north-east stands on the Lower Greensand outcrop. Beyond this the Weald Clay forms the second and wider vale, called 'The Vale of Sussex' which extends to the Wealden outcrop.

Looking south, the dipslope of the chalk shows the network of southward-draining valleys. Here they are dry because of the permeability of the chalk, but there is underground flow which ultimately emerges at the surface. Valleys east of Beacon Hill flow ultimately into the Lavant which feeds Chichester. Those to the west flow into the river Ems which enters Chichester Harbour at Emsworth. Beyond the Chalk we can see the London Clay plain of south Sussex with the city of Chichester in the middle. On the Isle of Wight we see its central spine of chalk which is the south limb of the syncline whose north limb is the South Downs on which we stand.

For a short walk we can return directly to the car park.

Alternatively, a most attractive route, adding about a mile, can take us a little to the south.

Go a further 200 yards towards Pen Hill and then sharp right down the South Downs Way. Pass one tumulus and continue to a second in some woodland. At the Y junction before reaching Telegraph House, turn sharp right back to the north-west, staying on the South Downs Way. After about 400 yards turn left at a waypost, leaving the South Downs Way. Drop down on a wide grassy track through gorse and scrub into the lower end of Bramshott Bottom, the valley which nearly notches the escarpment at its upper end.

At another waypost at the bottom of the hill turn right along the floor of the valley, passing a small enclosed pond on your left. Immediately after the pond avoid the main path up the coombe and fork left up a path which climbs gently up the floor of another wooded valley – Whitcombe Bottom. Towards the head of this valley, take any of the paths to the left which lead back up on to the South Downs Way along the escarpment. Turn left and follow this about 400 yards back to the car park.

Looking east from Beacon Hill.

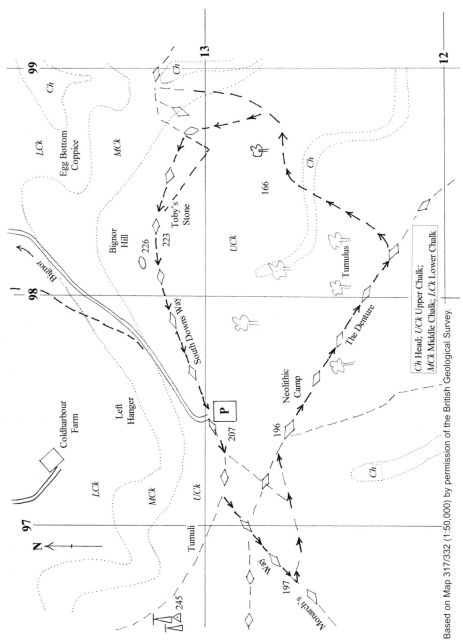

Based on Map 317/332 (1:50,000) by permission of the British Geological Survey.

3. BIGNOR HILL

OS 983133. Explorer map 121. Geological map: Chichester and Bognor Sheet 317/332 (1:50,000). 2½ miles.

Park at Bignor Hill car park (974130), a steep drive up from Bignor.

The whole walk is on Upper Chalk. Looking first north and then south, we can see the whole stratigraphic sequence from the Cretaceous Wealden sandstones of the High Weald to the Eocene of the coastal plain, with here and there a covering of younger superficial materials

THE WALK

Walk west, keeping the telegraph masts on your right. Follow the path whose fingerpost points to Gumber's Bothy along the edge of the National Trust property until you come to a stile. Turn left here, south-west along the Monarch Way, a straight part of Stane Street – a Roman road which connected Chichester with London. It is on an embankment called an 'agger'. A little further to the south-west is its highest point at 646ft (197m), probably used by the Romans as a survey point. The way beyond the stile may be blocked to pedestrians because erosion has made parts unsafe.

Turn very sharp back to the left along the boundary of the National Trust property and follow the direct path east-north-east. After 300 yards turn half right and proceed south-east along the South Downs Way, here called The Denture. In a field on the left one can just see the surface mounds which were part of a Neolithic camp. It has 13 entrances and is one of the largest causewayed enclosures ever discovered. It was damaged by ploughing in the past.

After about 500 yards we enter Barkhale Wood, and after a further 300 yards take a path to the left (north-east). This leads into a field. Cross the field across a dipslope valley. At the right hand end of the line of trees, leaving a barn on the right, take the track which leads directly up on to Bignor Hill. A short distance before the summit we pass Toby's Stone in the form of a horse-mounting block. It bears an inscription to James Wentworth Fitzwilliam Toby, once leader of the local hunt.

Bignor Hill is a forward promontory of the chalk scarp. Here you are standing on the Upper Chalk with the sequence of Middle Chalk, Lower Chalk, Upper Greensand, Gault, Lower Greensand, Hythe Beds and Atherfield Clay below in sequence to the north.

There is a good view to the northwest along the scarp face, and east over the wide flood plain of the Arun. We look northeast over the wide lowland on Weald Clay to the sandstone Wealden uplands beyond. Due north you can see the woodland and house of Bignor Park and to the east even the clump of Chanctonbury Ring is visible.

Note the wooded scarp below you, with the steep slope called the Left Hanger to the north-west and the steep hanger of Egg Bottom containing a coppice to the north-east. To the south-east is the wide expanse of Houghton Forest, too steep to have been cultivated. In the past this area had many skylarks and, in winter, flocks of fieldfares. To the south we can see over the coastal plain to the Channel.

Return to the car park west-south-west along the South Downs Way.

Bignor Hill, looking north.

Barkhale Wood.

TABLE OF SEDIMENTARY ROCKS

Sediment	Equivalent Rock	Grain-size
Gravel	Conglomerate & breccia	>2mm
Sand	Sandstone	2.0–0.05mm
Silt	Siltstone	0.05–0.002mm
Clay	Shale	<0.002mm
Calcareous mud & sand	Chalk & limestone	

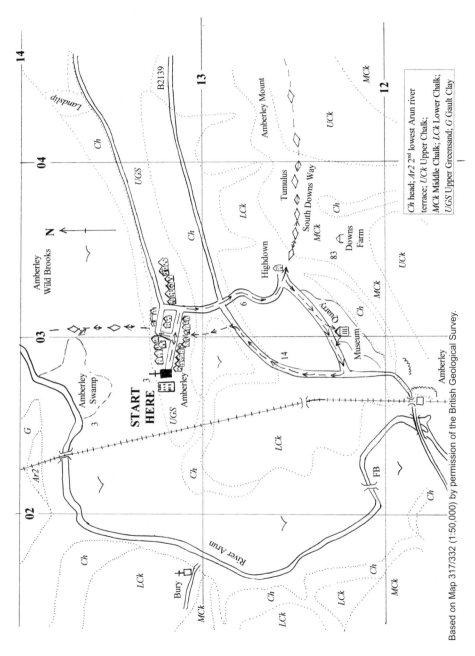

Based on Map 317/332 (1:50,000) by permission of the British Geological Survey.

Ch head; *Ar2* 2nd lowest Arun river terrace; *UCk* Upper Chalk; *MCk* Middle Chalk; *LCk* Lower Chalk; *UGS* Upper Greensand; *G* Gault Clay

4. AMBERLEY

OS 030132. Explorer map 121. Geological map: Chichester and Bognor Sheet 317/332 (1:50,000). 2½ or 3 miles.

Park in Amberley. One possibility is the car park outside the church, where there is a request for contributions to its maintenance.

Amberley Village lies parallel with the Downs on a little shelf of the Upper Greensand, which provides the southern border to that part of the Arun marshes called Amberley Wild Brooks. The village looks over these to the north towards the sandy Lower Greensand promontory of Greatham and Pulborough church beyond. Amberley is a popular place for artists because of its views.

THE WALK

Follow the Wey South Path out of the village, across some low ground floored by head. Cross the B2139. The path then ascends the Lower Chalk and Middle Chalk to reach the Upper Chalk at the top. The scarp crest is cut by south-flowing valleys floored with head.

Amberley: view to the west along the scarp.

Take the South Downs Way to the east, ascending Amberley Mount. Soon you will pass a small abandoned chalk quarry on the left. Note in it the stratification, fracturing and the absence of flints. Continue up the hill as far as two tumuli on the right. The summit on the Upper Chalk to the east shows its competence against erosion by the abundance of flints underfoot.

Go just high enough along this path to command a good view to the north and west. The feature is the valley of the Arun, its meanders, and the wide extent of the flood plain to the north, called Amberley Wild Brooks. This is low level ground covered in alluvium, and it is impounded behind the constriction of the River Arun as it cuts through the Chalk. The wider view extends west along the Chalk escarpment and north across the Lower Greensand outcrop, which circles around the western end of the Weald to appear high in the distance. To the north-east we see the intermediate heights of the Wealden Sandstone around Horsham.

Amberley church.

Return the same way, but at Highdown fork left down the High Titten on the Lower Chalk, being careful to avoid the wide track to the left which leads to Downs Farm. You will soon see on the left the white face of the large Amberley chalk pit, now containing an industrial museum. Do visit this if you have time: it shows most local crafts, including the uses of chalk. (telephone 01798 831370; website www.amberleymuseum.co.uk). High Titten has a broad verge suitable for horses and a bank of trees covered in old man's beard sweeping around the chalk pit edge. Half way down is a rest area with a shed and a seat overlooking the pit.

Turn right along the footpath beside the B2139 and follow this until you can turn left down a footpath which leads back to Amberley.

If you have time, walk northwards about 500 yards from the town across fields to Amberley Swamp. This is a derelict raised bog which grows upwards by successive additions of plant life above the floor of the basin on which it rests, so that its top profile is curved. The surrounding fields are edged by drainage ditches because this area is level and poorly drained, being only 10–13ft (3–4m) above sea level. Some are thought to have been laid out in a rectilinear pattern in Roman times. Amberley Wild Brooks nature reserve on blue clay soil lies about 1,000 yards (914m) to the north.

Now return to Amberley. This village is among the best places in the south of England to see vernacular architecture. It is a show village, 'although without any worthwhile building and without any definite focus' [*Nairn & Pevsner (2001) p.79*]. It has a wide variety of building materials: thatch, tile, brick, flint, half-timber, Bargate stone (from the Lower Greensand) and a little clunch. St Michael's church has a Norman framework and is flint-built but with sandstone pillars and corners. The feature is the chancel arch. The house almost opposite the vicarage has fossiliferous limestone around the doorway.

Walk a short way down the roadway to the right of the church. This passes a picnic area beside a stream and gives a good view of the north wall of Amberley Castle, now a country house hotel. This shows clearly how it is built on the Upper Greensand outcrop of fine sandstone. The building itself uses sandstone for corners and fills spaces with flint. On the corner of the building is a notice showing the height of the flood of November, 2000.

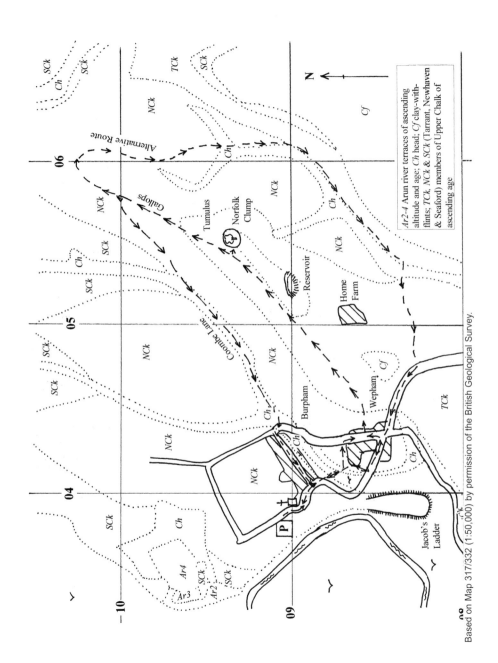

Ar2-4 Arun river terraces of ascending altitude and age; *Ch* head; *Cf* clay-with-flints; *TCk, NCk & SCk* (Tarrant, Newhaven & Seaford) members of Upper Chalk of ascending age

Based on Map 317/332 (1:50,000) by permission of the British Geological Survey.

5. BURPHAM & the ARUN VALLEY

OS 040088. Explorer map 121. Geological map: Chichester and Bognor Sheet 317/332 (1:50,000). 3¼ or 4 miles.
Park in Burpham (037091).

The Burpham area shows the contrast between the chalk Downs and the Arun river which breaks through them and, because of its small fall, is meandering. It is now tidal to beyond here.

Burpham is one of the loveliest villages in Sussex. As it lies in a fold of the Downs at the end of a three-mile cul-de-sac, it has a good chance of preserving its seclusion. It sits on a low cliff over a narrow, sluggish, forgotten channel of the Arun, now the haunt of kingfishers. There is some advantage in doing this walk in the morning rather than the afternoon because the view from the hill towards the west will be better. The sun will shine towards, rather than from behind, Arundel castle and the cathedral of St Philip Neri. Together these two buildings give 'one of the great town views of England, although very un-English: castle and dramatic pinnacled church at either end of a long ridge, backed by the Downs, with mellow brick houses tumbling down to the river Arun' [Nairn & Pevsner (2001) p86]. Both are 19th century constructions in medieval style.

Except for the flat alluvial plain of the Arun valley, and the head flooring the tributary channel through Burpham, the walk is on Upper Chalk. It everywhere contains flints. There is a distinction between the lower Newhaven Chalk member on the hill slopes, which contains some marl beds, and the upper Tarrant Chalk member

The Arun at North Stoke by F.L. Griggs.
[Lucas (1935) p.81]

57

crowning the hills, which does not. This explains the greater erosion resistance of the latter. The summit around the Norfolk Clump is floored with clay-with-flints.

THE WALK

Visit Burpham church. It is a mixture of styles: Saxon in the north wall, Norman in the north transept and the arch in the south transept, Early English in the chancel, and Decorated and Perpendicular in the windows. Note the use of chalk for piers in the nave arcade.

From the church return to the road and follow it south about 200 yards. Take the footpath which branches left to the neighbouring village of Wepham, with flint and half timbered cottages.

From Wepham take the footpath to the left of Home Farm up Perry Hill to Norfolk Clump (055093) on the Upper Chalk.

Note the views here, with Burpham in the foreground. The long promontory at the south end of the village is the site of a Saxon burh, built in the time of King Alfred. It is enclosed by earthworks overlooking the river and its Norman successor, Arundel Castle. The promontory is the result of circumdenudation by the Arun river on the west side and the small unnamed tributary which joins it on the east and south.

Note the Arun Valley beyond Burpham, dominated by the heights of Arundel Park and by Arundel Castle and the town to the south. This view gives a good impression of the way the Arun has maintained its valley. It must have originated at a time when the Wealden surface was a dome and before the unroofing of its crown exposed the edges of the constituent beds. It flowed south and maintained its course as the surrounding chalk was progressively exposed. Note, too, north-east of South Stoke (027100) the river meander which has been abandoned in favour of the active channel which swings close around the village.

Norfolk Clump crowns the hill top and there are views all around. There is a sign outside the clump saying 'No public Right of Way', but it is possible to walk around it and note the views in all directions.

For the shorter walk, continue along the same route into a straight called Gallops. After about 500 yards go sharp back to the left and return along a track almost parallel to the one you have ascended. After 500 yards join Coombe Lane which returns to Burpham village.

Note that there may be a 'Beware of the bull' sign beside a stile before reaching Coombe Lane. If so, it may be that discretion is the better part of valour, and that you should return by the route you came.

For the longer walk continue north-east along 'Gallops' and follow this track around a wide U-turn to the right, and then continue south-west with a steep slope up on the left for almost a mile. Then take a path to the right which returns to Wepham and Burpham.

Note the meander channel on your left as you return to the car park. The main flow of the river is now diverted into a straighter channel just west of the railway embankment.

Above: Arundel Castle from the hill above Burpham.

Below: Small cliff cut by the river below Burpham.

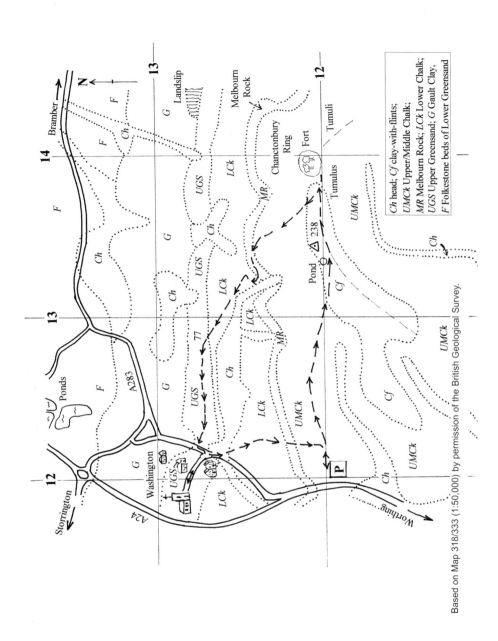

Based on Map 318/333 (1:50,000) by permission of the British Geological Survey.

Ch head; Cf clay-with-flints;
UMCk Upper/Middle Chalk;
MR Melbourn Rock; LCk Lower Chalk;
UGS Upper Greensand; G Gault Clay,
F Folkestone beds of Lower Greensand

6. CHANCTONBURY RING

OS 139121. Explorer map 121. Geological map: Brighton and Worthing sheet 318/333 (1:50,000). 3 miles.

Park beside the A24 road south of Washington at 120120 where there is also an information point.

THE WALK

Ascend the South Downs Way eastwards across the Upper Chalk. Note how much flint is underfoot. Before the deserted farmhouse at Frieslands there is old man's beard on the bushes and garden escapes of cotoneaster among the natural downland species. The ground can be very sticky when wet. After 500 yards you pass some disused flint workings. Following the signs continue along the track up towards Chanctonbury Hill. The summit itself, but not Chanctonbury Ring itself, has a covering of clay-with-flints.

On the left before you reach the trig point is a dewpond originally constructed around 1870 and which has now been restored by the Society of Sussex Downsmen.

Visit the trig point on Chanctonbury Hill (134121; 238m). Of all places in Sussex this must surely take the palm for its charm and magnificence of view. With little restriction the eye can range over sea, coast, South Downs, Weald and North Downs. In half an hour one could

Chanctonbury Ring before the 1987 storm, as seen from the east by F L Griggs.
[Lucas (1935) p.160]

identify such horizon points as Blackdown, Hascombe, St Martha's, Leith Hill, Reigate and Ashdown Forest. Look south to Cissbury Ring and note that this is on one of the prow-shaped hills in the Upper Chalk which are echeloned back from the main scarp but remain proud because of the occurrence of the 'quadratus zone' of stronger chalk (*see page 27*). Look down northwards to the scarp foot, where you can see the contrasting geology of the sand pit on Lower Greensand at Rock Common (128137). Note that the A283, which runs east from Washington towards Bramber, generally follows the outcrop of the Lower Greensand.

Look south down into nearby Well Bottom which cuts down into the Middle Chalk. This is the head of a deep dry valley, thought to have been developed largely in post glacial time. It feeds down into the Findon Valley, joining the sea at Worthing.

Now go on to Chanctonbury Ring itself. The discovery of flint implements shows that the hill was used in Neolithic time. It is capped by an Iron Age hill-fort, enclosing 3½ acres and defended by a low bank and ditch. These are best preserved on the south-west, where the single entrance occurs. Within the fort are the remains of two Roman buildings, one of which is a Romano-Celtic temple consisting of a square cella (enclosed area) surrounded by a verandah. The site appears to have been occupied by the Romans in the late 3rd century and the 4th century (*Nairn & Pevsner p365*). There is also a dewpond constructed in the 19th century.

The beech trees of the Ring were planted in 1760 by Charles Goring of Wiston. It is said that for months he carried water up the hill in bottles to aid their growth. When some blew over in the 1987 storm they exposed Iron Age and Roman archaeological features, and it was decided that the site should be excavated before any major replanting. From here you can just see Wiston House (153123) and the surrounding parkland through the trees in winter. Most of the 'Ring' has been replanted and protected by a sheep-proof fence until the new trees become established. It is astonishing to see the abundance of vegetation which thrives when sheep are excluded.

Take the path which goes diagonally down between the trig pillar and the Ring towards the north-west. Beware of the slipperiness caused by clay over chalk kept damp by overhanging trees. The acute steepening half way down is due to the outcrop of Melbourn Rock. At the bottom is a large disused quarry in the chalk much overgrown by trees (133124).

Looking up to Chanctonbury Ring.

Continue through a gate at a corner of the forest along a field path, crossing Lower Chalk to reach Washington village which stands on the small cuesta of Upper Greensand. One lane of cottages runs west to the church, rather disjoined and scrappy. The interesting thing is the variety of building materials at this meeting point of the Downs and the Weald. It includes two sorts of sandstone (green and dark brown) and clunch, as well as flint and brick. St Mary's church shows a mixture of sandstone and flint. It has a late perpendicular tower whose bell openings are filled with stone tracery, and a northern arcade whose arches and responds are rough work of about 1200 AD, but with intervening piers and abaci of the 13th century. The rest was rebuilt in 1867.

South of Washington (121125) branch left along a path which ascends the whole chalk escarpment, passing a disused quarry on the right. Turn right along the South Downs Way to regain the car park.

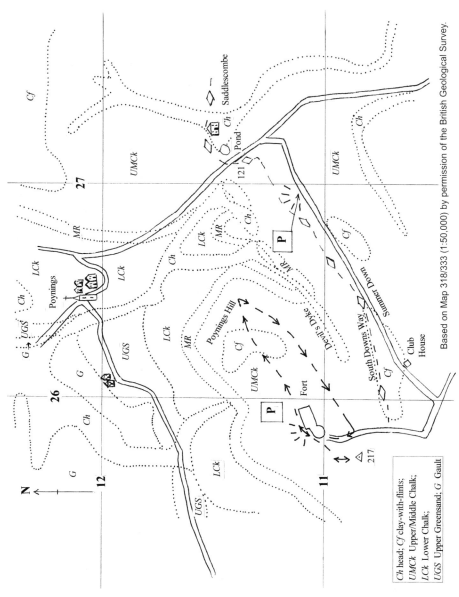

Based on Map 318/333 (1:50,000) by permission of the British Geological Survey.

Ch head; *Cf* clay-with-flints;
UMCk Upper/Middle Chalk;
LCk Lower Chalk;
UGS Upper Greensand; *G* Gault

7. POYNINGS & DEVIL'S DYKE

OS 258111 (Poynings) and 264111 (Devil's Dyke). Explorer map 122. Geological map: Brighton and Worthing Sheet 318/333 (1:50,000). 1 mile.

Park at the car park on Poynings Hill.

Note the magnificent views north over the Vale of Sussex, mainly on Weald Clay, before you see the Wealden Heights to the north-east and in the distance, to the north, the Lower Greensand Ridge which masks the still more distant North Downs. There are look-out panoramic diagrams identifying all visible features, stone seats and a plaque with a verse from Psalm 104.

Poynings from Devil's Dyke by F L Griggs.
[Lucas (1935) p. 219]

THE WALK

From the car park walk first to visit the trig pillar (712ft; 217m), standing on an ancient bank. Then walk north-east past the fort and the lateral banks. After about 500 yards turn sharp back to the right. Immediately below you is Devil's Dyke, one of the most conspicuous hangers cut back into the chalk escarpment. Its bottom has cut down to the Middle Chalk but has to some extent been filled by head.

The hilltop is surrounded by the excavations of an Iron Age fort now covered with trees. It is all on Upper Chalk with a patch of clay-with-flints at the north-east end of the fort. Middle and Lower Chalk are exposed on the scarp slope to the north with the village of Poynings on a patch of head (loose materials slumped down the hillslope by gravity) which raise it above the underlying Gault Clay. The road along the foot of the hill from Fulking to Poynings runs mainly along the Upper Greensand cuesta.

Devil's Dyke, looking up . . .

66

The north-east/south-west trend of the escarpment between Devil's Dyke and Wolstonbury Hill (284137) is due to a minor anticline whose axis runs east-west about a mile north of Poynings.

Return to the car park along the path beside the Devil's Dyke.

For an extra view on your return journey, stop at the car park 1 mile down Summer Down Road (269112). This looks north over the Devil's Dyke, Poynings and the Vale of Sussex.

. . . and looking down.

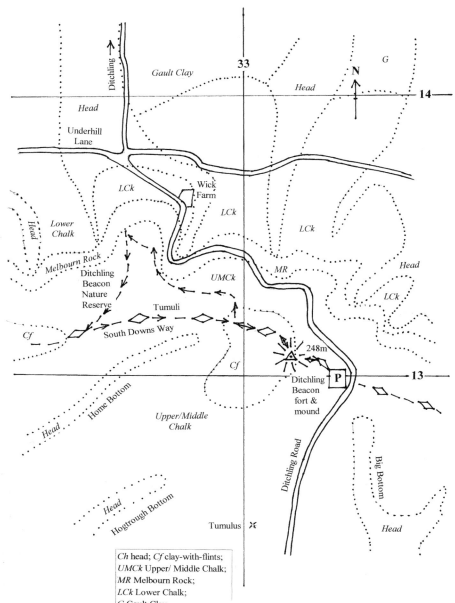

Based on Map 318/333 (1:50,000) by permission of the British Geological Survey.

8. DITCHLING BEACON

OS 332131. Explorer map 122. Geological map: Brighton and Worthing sheet 318/333 (1:50,000). 1½ miles
Park at the Ditchling Beacon car park (National Trust).

The view here is magnificent. You can look west to Wolstonbury Hill, beyond to Devil's Dyke and on a clear day as far as Chanctonbury Ring to the west and Beachy Head cliff to the east.

THE WALK

South of the car park lie the ploughed-out remains of an Iron Age fort with an information board at its north-western corner. There is a trig pillar in the centre of the hill fort and a viewing plinth. This is the third

Looking north-east from Ditchling Beacon over Westmeston.

Looking north-west from Ditchling Beacon over the village.

highest point on the Sussex Downs at 814ft (248m), after Littleton and Linch Hills.

Note the surrounding geology. Immediately around the car park the surface has a covering of clay-with-flints. Below this and all around is the Upper Chalk. On the escarpment to the north is the familiar sequence: Middle Chalk and Lower Chalk on the scarp and in the distance the high ground of the Weald Sandstone. The whole of the relatively low ground between the two is the thickly populated Vale of Sussex. But in detail this consists of three east-west bands: the Gault Clay vale at our feet; then the cuesta of the Lower Greensand on which stand Hassocks, Ditchling and the hamlet of Streat; and beyond this the Weald Clay vale.

Immediately to the north of the Beacon note the series of almost equidistant re-entrants in the scarp face, owing their origin to undersapping where water percolating through the Chalk emerges at the contact with the Gault Clay. This is the origin of many northward flowing streams from the foot of the South Downs into the Vale of Sussex. The valleys thus formed are filled with downwashed head.

Note immediately to the west of the Beacon the heads of two dipslope valleys, Home Bottom and Hogtrough Bottom. These join about a mile further south and run into the larger valley which enters Brighton at Patcham and ultimately reaches the sea at Brighton by the Palace Pier.

Walk about 300 yards west along the South Downs Way. Then take the mainly wooded footpath down to the northwest to visit the Ditchling Beacon nature reserve belonging to the Sussex Wildlife Trust. This crosses the scarpface exposures of the Middle and Lower Chalk. Note flowers and butterflies. The orchids are of particular interest including the burnt, fragrant, frog, musk and bee types.

Just above an old quarry at the hill foot take the marked path which turns sharp left and ascends again to the South Downs Way on the summit. Turn east and return to the car park.

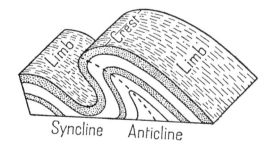

THE FOLDING OF THE LANDSCAPE

The diagram on the left illustrates the meanings of syncline, anticline and axial plane (the dashed line).

The diagram below illustrates the meaning of dip and strike.

[Source Holmes, pages 71 & 73]

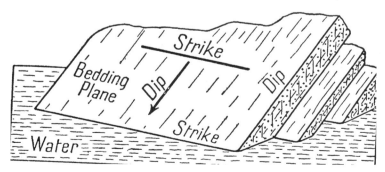

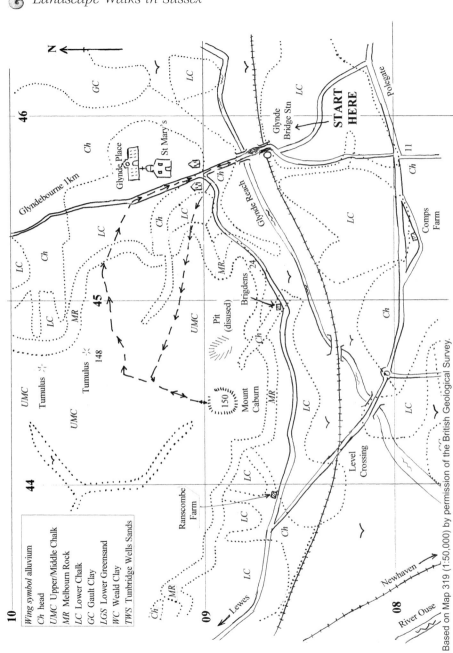

Based on Map 319 (1:50,000) by permission of the British Geological Survey.

Wing symbol alluvium
Ch head
UMC Upper/Middle Chalk
MR Melbourn Rock
LC Lower Chalk
GC Gault Clay
LGS Lower Greensand
WC Weald Clay
TWS Tunbridge Wells Sands

9. MOUNT CABURN & BEDDINGHAM

OS 445078. Explorer maps 122 &123. Geological map: Lewes sheet 319 (1:50,000). 2½ miles.

Park in Glynde: it is possible sometimes to leave a car in the car park at Glynde Bridge railway station.

*The Ouse above
Lewes by F L Griggs.
[Lucas (1935) p.276]*

Mount Caburn deserves special consideration. Major folding determined the main layout of the Weald, with the High Weald at the core and the North and South Downs defining its limits. But within this there are subsidiary folds. One of these is an east-west anticline (upfold) whose axis here runs between Caburn and Itford hills. The cross-section below shows that the most significant effect on the landscape is the dropping of the area to the west of this (424079), known as The Brooks, so that it forms an extensive alluvial flat on Gault Clay bounded on north and south by higher ground on the Lower Chalk.

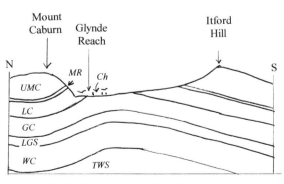

Based on Map 319 by permission of the British Geological Survey.

THE WALK

Ascend Caburn Hill by the path that leads upwards from opposite the post office at the southern end of Glynde. After 1,000 yards take the track to the left to the summit. Note the deep trench of Caburn Bottom to the north-west of the summit, the upper end of a deep erosion valley in the chalk which drains into the Ouse near Lewes. This valley seems to be consequent upon the base level provided by the Ouse's incision of the Chalk which has given the site of Lewes.

The summit was of great importance as a defensive position in ancient time. It was first settled in the Bronze Age and much developed in the Iron Age. The top was only vulnerable from the north and here a double line of ditch and bank was built. There is also evidence of a well being dug. The impressive defences visible today date mainly from the Roman invasion in 43 AD. It seems that a deeper ditch was dug to protect against the Romans and the resulting rampart is still six metres above the adjoining ditch. But the Romans apparently took the fort quickly, and excavation has revealed that they set alight a wooden gateway to gain entrance. This was not the end of settlement, however. Pottery finds show that it was occupied until well into the second century.

Looking up to Mount Caburn hill-fort.

Note the series of re-entrants in the scarp front, best seen picked out by the late afternoon sun. Despite its undistinguished elevation, the prominence of its position gives summit of Mount Caburn one of the most magnificent views in Sussex. To the south-east is the escarpment on the south side of the anticline running from Firle Beacon west through Beddingham Hill (with two radio masts) to Itford Hill to the south. West of Itford Hill we can see the valley of the Ouse and its meanders to the sea out of the low level flood plain called The Brooks. The altitude of its surface is only about two metres above sea level. South of

The view over the Ouse Valley to the sea from Caburn.

Lewes we can see two hillocks called, from north to south, Upper Rise and Lower Rise. They are of Lower Chalk directly on Gault. There is no Upper Greensand in the area.

To make an attractive circuit return to your car by going back along the way you ascended, but continuing on where it turns down towards Glynde and proceeding a further 200 yards before following a track down to the right which joins the Glynde–Ringmer road just north of Glynde Place. This is a large courtyard house built of flint in the 1560s, and open to the public during the season (telephone 01273 512123; www.sussextourism.org.uk). Next to it is St Mary's built in the 1760s, and the only purely classical church in the county.

Return to your car down this road through Glynde.

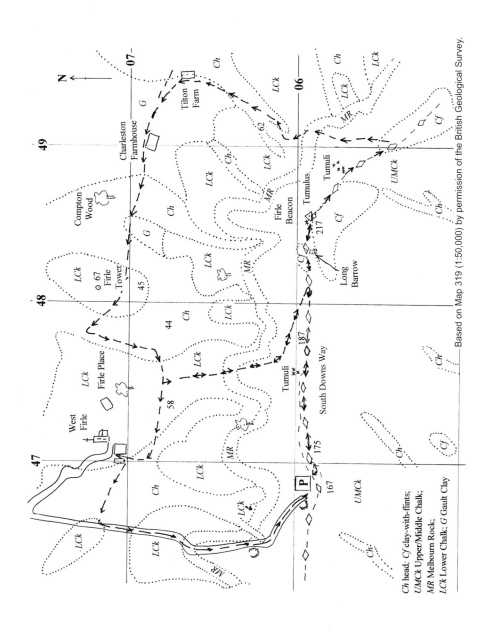

N

Based on Map 319 (1:50,000) by permission of the British Geological Survey.

Ch head: *Cf* clay-with-flints;
UMCk Upper/Middle Chalk;
MR Melbourn Rock;
LCk Lower Chalk; *G* Gault Clay

10. FIRLE BEACON

OS 485059. Explorer map 123. Geological map: Lewes Sheet 319 (1:50,000). 2, 3½ or 5¼ miles.

Approach along the A27(T) and take the road south past Firle village to the car park at the top of the hill.

THE WALK

Go eastwards along the South Downs Way. The underlying rock is undifferentiated Middle and Upper Chalk as seen from the flints underfoot. The top of the cliff has an outcrop of the harder Melbourn Rock which forms the top of the Lower Chalk.

The path passes a number of round barrows and, after ½ mile, a Neolithic long barrow. This is more than 100ft (30m) long and 8ft (2.4m) high, surrounded by ditches which enclose it except for a narrow causeway at the south-east corner. In places lynchets are visible, probably dating from the Roman period. About 200 yards further takes us to the trig pillar on Firle Beacon. Immediately around this are more than 50 early Bronze Age bowl barrows. Most appear to have been excavated and from one came a bronze pin of central European type, now lost.

Firle Beacon opens some of the most impressive scenery of the South Downs. It dominates the chalk outcrop between the Ouse and Cuckmere valleys, a distance of no more than five miles. The north-facing scarp is straight and bold from Firle Beacon to Alfriston (520033). West of Firle Beacon it becomes more broken as deep coombes have developed in the chalk face. These are best seen from Mount Caburn visible three miles to the north-west, which emphasizes their impressive appearance in the late afternoon sun. Looking north from Firle Beacon, note the near-rectilinear field and road patterns around the villages of Ripe and Chalvington. It has been suggested that this dates from Roman centuriation.

Throughout this section the ridge crest on Middle and Upper Chalk is continuous, for none of the dry valleys has succeeded in cutting back through the scarp. The dry valley system on the dipslope to the south is very well developed, with a tendency for the main valleys to run in a south-south-west direction.

Along almost its entire length the scarp is fronted by a bench developed on the beds of the Lower Chalk. On this bench are Pearson's Wish promontory (495064), Charleston Farmhouse (*see below*) and Firle Tower (481072), all visible from the Beacon. The villages of Firle, Alciston and Berwick lie on the spring line at the base of the chalk where the scarp-slope valley intersects the impermeable underlying Gault Clay. The lower ground formed by valleys out of the combes is generally floored with head.

Look north across the geological sequence of the Vale of Sussex. The slope beneath us falls away over exposures of the Middle and Lower Chalk and then, in order, we see the Gault Clay, the narrow Lower Greensand along which the railway runs and, beyond that, the Weald Clay with the town of Hailsham. Beyond that we see the rising ground to the Wealden Sandstone in the background.

Looking down on Charleston Farmhouse from Firle Beacon.

From Firle Beacon there are three options of route:

1. For the shortest walk return to the car park by the same route.

2. To visit Firle (officially known as West Firle), return along the South Downs Way about 300 yards west from the Beacon and take the path which runs diagonally downhill to the north-west. This then passes the Firle Plantation of trees and turns left along a flint wall before turning right into the village. Firle is an attractive village. The church is built of flint within a limestone framework. It dates from the 14th and 15th centuries and contains monuments to the Gage family, including a window designed by John Piper, and some exceptional brasses. Nearby is Firle Place, built for Sir John Gage, vice-chamberlain to Henry VIII, who died in 1557. The central hall is Tudor, the rest more recent. It is open to the public (telephone 01273 858335; www.firleplace.co.uk).

To return to the car park from Firle it is necessary to leave the village by the way you entered it, but turn right after the last house and follow the path west to the road called Firle Bostal. Turn left into the road and return to the car park along it.

3. To visit Charleston Farmhouse from Firle Beacon continue south-east from the Beacon along the South Downs Way about 400 yards, and then turn sharp back to the left along a path down the escarpment past Tilton Farm to Charleston Farmhouse. This was a centre of the Bloomsbury group between 1907 and 1930. It has a remarkable interior, housing important domestic work of the painters Vanessa Bell, sister of Virginia Woolf, and Duncan Grant. There are textiles, pottery, carpets and wall paintings in each room with characteristic flower and figure motifs. After the death of Duncan Grant in 1978, the Charleston Trust was formed. It has restored the house and its contents plus the garden (telephone 01323 811626; www.charleston.org.uk).

Return to the car park by following the path towards Firle for about $\frac{2}{3}$ mile. Turn left for about 300 yards, right along Comp Lane for about $\frac{1}{2}$ mile and then left again to follow the path up Firle Bostal to the South Downs Way and the car park.

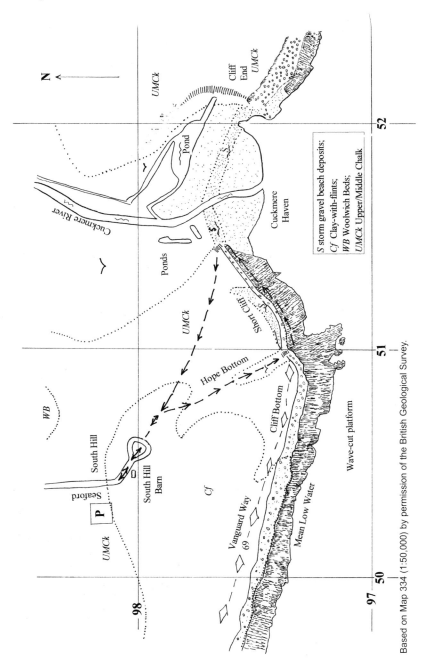

Based on Map 334 (1:50,000) by permission of the British Geological Survey.

11. HOPE BOTTOM & SHORT CLIFF, SEAFORD

OS 510973. Explorer map 123. Geological map: Eastbourne sheet 334 (1:50,000). 2 miles.

Park at the car park at South Hill 505981 by South Hill Barn at the eastern end of Seaford.

As this walk is partly along the beach backed by a cliff it is important to consult a tide table and to visit the beach preferably at ebb tide. Because of the amount and potential suddenness of cliff falls, it is best to keep at least 10ft (3m) back from the cliff top edge. On the beach it is safest to walk at least 25ft (8m) away from the cliff foot.

Seaford Head (493977) has cliffs in Upper Chalk 279ft (85m) high. This was once a defensive point, and it is marked by a circumferential ditch and tumulus. South-east of here the cliff line follows the strike of the rocks and is marked by vertical joints.

The Seven Sisters from Short Cliff, Seaford.

THE WALK

Walk down through a large turning circle for cars and after about 300 yards fork right on to a path that leads down Hope Valley to access to the beach at Hope Bottom (510973), a hanging valley above a wave-cut bench. Note the view eastwards to the famous Seven Sisters, separated by hanging valleys where the sea has cut back into the cliff.

Walk down to the beach at Hope Bottom. Its outer part is a wave-cut platform. The outermost promontory to the south, visible at low water, is called the Mares. It shows the rectilinear structure in the underlying chalk. On the platform, waves roll pebbles along joints which are roughly at right angles to the shore line erode 'gutters', often sinuous in form and up to 3ft (1m) deep. These drain the platform as the tide ebbs.

A view up the Cuckmere from South Hill nature reserve, Seaford.

Walk east along the beach below Short Cliff. Note the exposure of the Upper and Middle Chalk in the cliff. A notable feature is the many solution pipes. Nineteen have been recorded on the beach and five are exposed in the cliff. Those on the cliff face are vertical shafts containing some brown infilling material. Those on the beach resemble eroded stone-built well heads, although they are completely natural. All are caused by aggressive solution with acidified water followed by infilling with rubble and clay.

The chalk, being largely built of the remains of sea creatures, contains many fossils. It is worth examining a few pieces with a hand lens (x10 or x20) to see if you can see shells or shell casts.

Climb the cliff again at Cuckmere Haven. This gives a good view over the lower part of the Cuckmere River with its meanders undercutting the cliffs, the sandy and shingly coastal spit cut by an outlet channel and the impounded lagoon. The river mouth is deflected eastwards by the longshore drift of the spit. West of the lagoon is a salt marsh covered with succulent vegetation.

Note especially the contrast in coastal character between this and Hope Bottom because of the resistance of the chalk at the former and the weakness of the alluvial mouth of the Cuckmere which has allowed the sea to form a bay between two chalk headlands.

Return to the car park by the direct track.

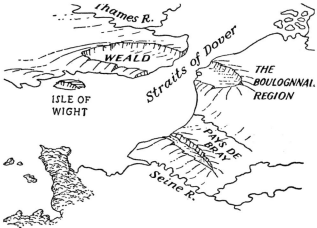

The relationship of the Weald to northern France. [Source: Lobeck p. 520]

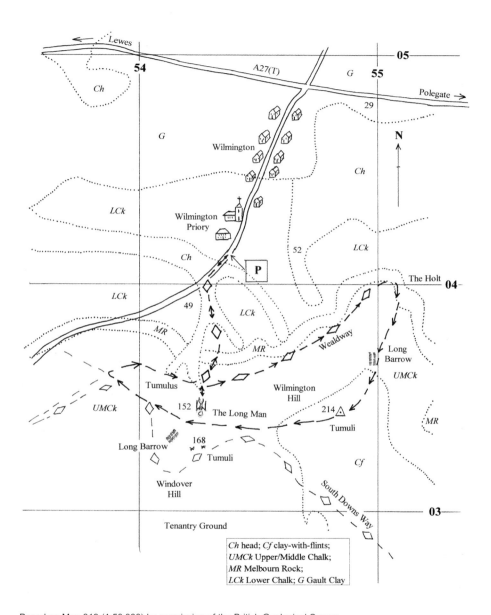

Based on Map 319 (1:50,000) by permission of the British Geological Survey.

12. WILMINGTON the LONG MAN

OS 545042 (Wilmington). Explorer map 123. Geological map: Lewes Sheet 319 (1:50,000). 2½ miles.

Park at Wilmington Priory at the southern end of the village, where there is a small car park with picnic site and public toilet.

The north half of the village and the line of the A27(T) road are on Gault Clay, but the church and the Priory stand on the higher ground of Lower Chalk. There is a large ancient yew in the garden.

Wilmington has two buildings of interest. The church of St Mary and St Peter is of flint edged with limestone. It has a Norman chancel, an Early English aisle and a Victorian chancel arch. The pulpit is Jacobean and there is a small seated sculpture in the chancel. There is a large and ancient yew in the churchyard.

The Long Man of Wilmington.

Next door to it is Wilmington Priory, which was founded by Benedictines from Normandy before 1100. It lacks a chapel because it always used the parish church. The southern doorway leads into a large room which must have been the main entrance. There is a 14th century hall with two polygonal turrets on the south wall. Its large window is Elizabethan or later. Above the porch is the prior's chapel, which is stepped and has ogee-headed windows. The building is in private ownership and not open to the public.

View to the sea from above the Long Man.

THE WALK

Walk south down the main street and fork left along the track up the hill towards the Long Man until you reach a T-junction with an east-west track. This roughly parallels, but is above, the line of the hard Melbourn Rock, the lowest bed of the Middle Chalk.

It is possible to divert 100 yards up or so to see the Long Man. This is the largest representation of the human figure in Europe, being over 200ft (60m) in height. The original trenches cut through the chalk have now been picked out by concrete infilling. There are various theories of its origin varying from an Iron Age fertility figure to Alfred Watkins' view that he is a 'dodman' holding two posts for surveying and establishing ley lines. It received no mention until the 18th century but could be Celtic, Saxon or even Viking in origin, or perhaps associated with the monks of Wilmington Priory nearby. It is almost certainly not as old as the barrows and flint mines above. It is best viewed from Wilmington.

Return to the Wealdway, turn to the east and walk about 400 yards until you see a track sharply back to the right leading diagonally upwards. Note the steep manger called The Holt just beyond this turn.

Climb this track to the top of Windover Hill (542033; 617ft/188m high), but before reaching the top look south-westwards down the unspoilt dry valley of Deep Dean, draining into the Cuckmere via Deep Dean (539025) and Park Bottom (532024).

From Windover Hill you can just see the cliffs of Newhaven and to the west the white horse carved into the turf at High and Over. Northwards the view extends over the clay lowlands towards the heights of the Weald in the distance. Note that the east-west railway line runs along the Gault Clay, but beyond this, about a mile away and parallel to the foot of the scarp, there runs a low ridge of Lower Greensand which separates the Gault Clay lowland in the foreground from the Weald Clay lowland beyond it.

On its northern crest Windover Hill has a small group of Neolithic flint mines using shallow workings. The depression on the hilltop east of the Long Man is an example. Such pits occur in many places on the Downs, notably within the ramparts of the Iron Age hill fort at Cissbury, where they are believed to have been worked in the Neolithic and early Bronze Age. Before the Bronze Age flint was in great demand for tools and weapons. The typical flint mine was about 4m deep and anything from 3–6m across. In section it had a small surface opening but widened underground. The rounded hollows we see today are due to later collapse. The mound around the workings represents the spoil of unwanted chalk and other rubble. The Upper Chalk contains the most suitable flint band, and the prehistoric flint mines such as those at Cissbury and between Windover and Wilmington hills (545034) are therefore from this horizon. The presence of flint also led to other forms of human occupation as evidenced by the abundance of barrows. Note the downland flowers in this area.

South of the mines is a Stone Age long barrow 180ft (55m) long and 50ft (15m)wide at its broader north-east end. The side ditches, which are still visible, are slightly inturned at the ends. On Windover Hill, south of the Long Man, is a Bronze Age bowl barrow over 120ft (37m) in diameter which covered a cremation urn. Further round barrows can be seen south and east of the Long Man.

Follow the track along the top of the escarpment, or else the South Downs Way which skirts the south of the summit, towards the west. Follow either down until they join the Wealdway. Turn east and follow this back to return to Wilmington.

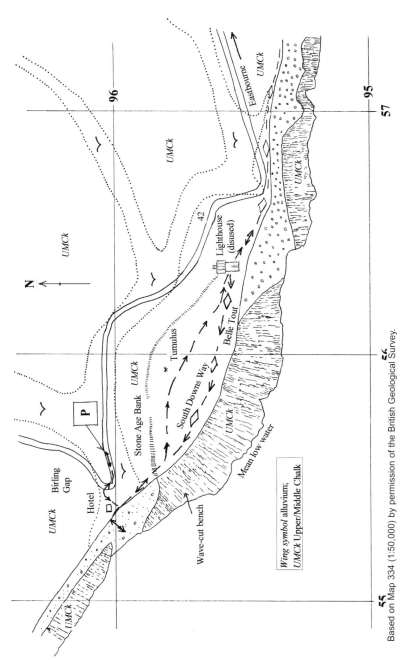

Based on Map 334 (1:50,000) by permission of the British Geological Survey.

Wing symbol alluvium;
UMCk Upper/Middle Chalk

13. EASTWARDS FROM BIRLING GAP

OS 553960. Explorer map 123. Geological map: Eastbourne sheet 334 (1:50,000). 1½ miles.

Park at Birling Gap car park (556961) on the B2103 about 300 yards east of the hotel.

The National Trust acquired the Gap under its Enterprise Neptune Scheme (set up to protect as much as possible of the coastline) and has erected a viewing platform to enable you to see the Seven Sisters. There are steps down to the beach.

If you plan to spend some time on the beach, special care is needed to make sure that the tide is not rising and that you do not risk being cut off without access to Birling Gap.

THE WALK

When on the beach note the contrast between the near-vertical soft white chalk cliffs and the near-horizontal wave-cut platform covered with flints eroded out of the Chalk. At low tide the platform is on chalk, covered here and there with a low tabular cover of flint.

This beach is the best place to view rocks and fossils along this coast. Each fragment of chalk contains many fossils, being mainly built of them. They include small bivalves called lamellibranchs (American pelecypods), such as twin shelled *Volviceramus*, an ancient oyster called *Platyceramus* which can be up to 30 cm in diameter, *Uintcrinus*, which is a relative of the sea urchin but had long tentacles and can be up to 8cm, and *Micraster*, a sea urchin up to 7cm in diameter.

As you observe the cliffs you will see that away from the steps in both directions there are clear strata of chalk marked by bedding planes and lines of flints. However, around the lowest point around the steps the upper half of the profile is more jumbled, with broken flints and an absence of horizontal stratification. This is because this low area of the cliff is the seaward extremity of a hanging valley called The Wish (556963), followed by the road, which is occupied by coombe deposits, also called head, here mapped as alluvium. These are loose materials which gravity has brought down the slopes on both sides. This downward creep is due to the process known as solifluxion, thought to

Looking west from above Birling Gap to the Seven Sisters and Seaford Head.

have been due to accelerated downslope sliding over frozen ground during the Ice Age.

Now look at the horizontally bedded chalk below the coombe deposits. This is the Upper Chalk, containing bands of flint. Note the diagonal bands running through the horizontal bands at a steep angle. Geologists are not sure how they formed. The layer of flints at the bottom of the cliff (and on the beach) are flat and plate-like. You can follow this band all along the Seven Sisters to Cuckmere Haven. The deposition of the flint must have been related to the alkalinity of water full of calcareous material.

Now note how little chalk there is in the beach material which is well over 90 per cent flints. This is because the calcium carbonate is easily destroyed by abrasion and solution, while the flint (silicon dioxide) is highly resistant to both.

Climb up again from the beach to Birling Gap. Go through the car park and take the path forking upwards to the right along the cliff top towards the old Belle Tout lighthouse. Views to the beach show a wide wave-cut platform in the Chalk and the sea often discoloured by its content of chalky material.

Most of this area lies within a large ditch enclosure which reaches the edge of the cliff near Birling Gap at the west end and near the lighthouse at the east end – clearly an important defensive site in the Stone Age, though its area has since been reduced by cliff erosion.

The significant feature of this walk is the view forward to Beachy Head from near the lighthouse (now private property) and backwards to the Seven Sisters, both of which are well displayed.

Return to the car park from the lighthouse by the lower path to the north which passes a large clump of trees and generally keeps to the right, parallel to the Stone Age bank.

HOW THE FLINT WAS FORMED

There are three theories of the formation of flint:

1. After the emergence of the Chalk from the sea, silica gel was deposited along paths of ground water movement and later hardened into flint.

2. There was a concentration of silica around the bodies and fossils of small creatures.

3. It was formed by the chemical segregation of silica while the Chalk was being deposited under the sea.

On the whole, a combination of the second and third causes seems most likely, because fossil organisms are sometimes found at the core of flints, while there seldom seems to be a clear relationship between the occurrence of flints and post-emergence groundwater movements.

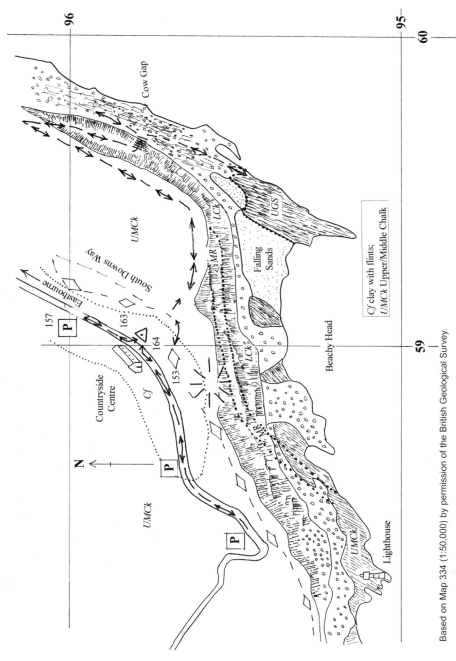

Based on Map 334 (1:50,000) by permission of the British Geological Survey.

92

14. BEACHY HEAD

OS 589955. Explorer map 123. Geological map: Eastbourne sheet 334 (1:50,000). Approximately 2 miles.

Start at one of the car parks near the Beachy Head Countryside Centre.

The car park beside the Beachy Head Inn in the Countryside Centre stands on a patch of clay-with-flints. It is across the road from the trig pillar, and it has toilets and a café, but it is open only in summer. Remember that this walk involves walking along a beach backed by cliffs, and it is therefore important to check the state of the tide before proceeding.

THE WALK

Visit the trig pillar across the road, then go about 250 yards to the southwest to the viewing point at Beachy Head. This gives good views over Eastbourne to the north-east, the chalk plateau to the north and over the sea and foreshore to the south. This is a good area for geological

The view east to Eastbourne from Beachy Head.

study because it includes the whole thickness of the Chalk and some of the underlying deposits. The highest point is at the top of the Upper Chalk, while the base of the Lower Chalk can be seen at the high water mark at Cow Gap.

Go carefully to the cliff edge and look down 530ft (160m) to the Beachy Head Lighthouse built in 1902. The Upper Chalk, lined by courses of black flint nodules, forms the spectacular cliff that towers more than 150 m above the lighthouse. Note the wave-cut bench cut across the chalk exposed on the shore below the shingle. The rocks here dip north-

Beachy Head with the lighthouse below.

westwards and, when the beach is exposed at low tide, the Upper Greensand exposures stand up as prominent ridges along the beach.

To the south, the English Channel stretches to the horizon. On a clear day you can see east across four main geological areas: 1. the Chalk under your feet; 2. the low ground and coastal inlet of the Gault and Wealden clays at and beyond Eastbourne; 3. the Wealden Beds around Hastings and the Fairlight Cliffs; and 4. the Dungeness headland on sea-borne alluvium.

Return to the Countryside Centre and take the path across the road which leads down to the beach at Cow Gap. This begins with a steep slope down the chalk but turns left at the bottom and roughly follows the edge of the cliff to the north-east. After about 700 yards it skirts a slumped area on the right. Just beyond this turn sharp back to the right at a sign saying 'Cow Gap Beach Access' and some steps. Descend these, and after a short walk and a final steep flight of steps leads to the beach at Cow Gap

Cow Gap, like Whitbread Hole to the east, is formed by eroding glacial meltwater followed by solifluxion of the material down the side slopes. In the cliff a base about 7m thickness of Upper Greensand is overlain by the part of the Lower Chalk called the Glauconitic Marl. The shore platform is cut across Gault and Upper Greensand. Where the shore is relatively clear of pebbles it is possible to see the underlying contact between the Gault and the Upper Greensand, whose greenish colour derives from the mineral glauconite. The Gault Clay below it appears as a soft black beach platform with a dense network of fine cracks. Since it is a weak material, undercutting by the sea has caused repeated cliff falling.

The strata contain many visible fossils and casts including bivalves, sponges with their spicules, and the burrows of marine worms and prawns often causing honeycomb weathering on its surface. Note also that some horizons are 'proud' of others, generally because they are of sandstone.

Above the Upper Greensand is the Glauconitic Marl. It contains rounded hard white calcareous concretions which often hold sponge remains. Small brown phosphatic nodules, usually less than 2cm, sometimes contain fossils, the commonest being ammonites, bivalves and brachiopods.

Above the Glauconitic Marl the rest of the Lower Chalk is often richly fossiliferous and shows an alternation of dark grey marls and hard white limestone beds. Echinoids, bivalves, sponges and ammonites occur throughout the sequence. It also contains iron nodules. An important fossiliferous horizon lies about 33ft (10m) above the Glauconitic Marl and has yielded many ammonites, brachiopods, and sponges. All beds are intensely burrowed, especially by the marine worm *Chondrites* which leaves branching tunnels 1–2mm in diameter.

Now look down the beach beyond the Gault Clay and you will see at least one more outcrop of the Upper Greensand. The reason is this: since the Gault Clay is weak, the attack of the sea has caused it to slump and carry down its overburden of Upper Greensand along a strip fault parallel to the coast. Each slip therefore lowers a strip of Upper Greensand to sea level. As a result its outcrop is repeated no fewer than five times on the foreshore, each outcrop forming a steep-sided ridge. The sea has eroded these ridges into some bizarre shapes, picking out the bedding planes and joints to produce a local relief of up to 1.5 m. The largest exposure of the Upper Greensand forms the jutting reef of the Head Ledge.

Return to the car park by the same route.

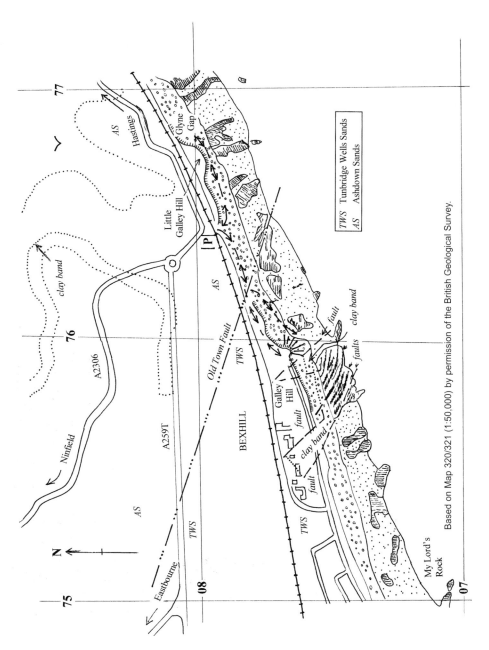

Based on Map 320/321 (1:50,000) by permission of the British Geological Survey.

TWS Tunbridge Wells Sands
AS Ashdown Sands

15. GALLEY HILL, BEXHILL

OS 758076. Explorer map 124. Geological map: Hastings and Dungeness sheet 320/321 (1:50,000). 1½ miles.

When coming by car, drive through Bexhill to the car park where the A259 reaches the sea between Galley Hill (759077) and Glyne Gap (765079).

THE WALK

Cross the railway line, turn right and follow the path beside it to the west about 700 yards towards the top of Galley Hill. About half way along we cross the Old Town Fault and move from Ashdown Sands on to Tunbridge Wells Sands. Galley Hill is the highest point on the coast on the latter.

Note the view out to sea. Beyond the beach one can see the wave cut platform in Wealden rocks.

Galley Hill, Bexhill, from Little Galley Hill.

Return East and go down to the beach near the car park. Walk west along the beach, looking at the rock exposures below Galley Hill.

The lower part of the cliff is masked by landslip. The lowest unit visible is a red clay which shows a honeycombed effect where erosion has picked out a network of thin hard iron veins. The overlying succession is from bottom to top: iron-veined sandstone; grey silty clay; whitish silt; grey silt; and thicker iron-veined sandstone. The last thins out eastwards into a thin grey clay. Above this is more sandstone which weathers grey but is much lighter in colour when fresh. It thins out eastwards. Over it is a dark siltstone whose base is a thin conglomerate of plant debris and sandstone fragments derived from erosion of the underlying sandstone. This thickens eastwards.

Essentially the same geological sequence can be traced eastwards to the small headland (759076). Just before this there is a small anticlinal fold in the beds.

Walk east from Galley Hill about 700 yards to the small cliff beyond the access to the car park. This is Little Galley Hill. It is composed mostly of gently north-easterly dipping Ashdown sandstones. The lowest bed exposed is a light brown ferruginous sandstone overlain by a thin pebble bed 23cm thick. This contains quartz pebbles, black plant debris, and fragments of soft fine-grained sandstone, all in a sandy matrix. The sandstone fragments are derived from the underlying sandstone bed by erosion. We can see this from the sharp irregular base of the conglomerate carved into the bed below by rapid river flow. Note also how the coarse conglomerate becomes finer grained upwards and grades into the overlying sandstone. This shows how the speed of the current decreased to allow the deposition of the sand on a former eroded surface. The sea is actively eroding the cliffs, as can be seen from their unstable character and the wave-cut platform of resistant ferruginous sandstone at their base.

Beyond Little Galley Hill is Glyne Gap. Dinosaur footprints have been found here in the lowest sandstone bed exposed on the shore at low tide. These are mainly of the Iguanodon and are up to 60cm long from the heel to the end of the central toe. There are also blackened carbonized tree trunks which must have grown prior to the major rise in sea level (the 'Flandrian transgression') following the end of the Ice Age.

Return to the car park along the beach, ascending the staircase and crossing the railway line.

Wave-cut platform at Galley Hill.

It is also highly recommended to visit the Bexhill Museum in Egerton Road (737071) 200 yards west of the De la Warr Pavilion (telephone 01424 787950; www.bexhillmuseum.co.uk). It contains a good display of Wealden geology, with particular reference to the Iguanodon remains. There is also an example of polished Purbeck marble showing many snail-like *Viviparus* shells. A good description of the local geology can be found in the booklet by Ken Brooks, *Geology and Fossils of the Hastings Area* available here.

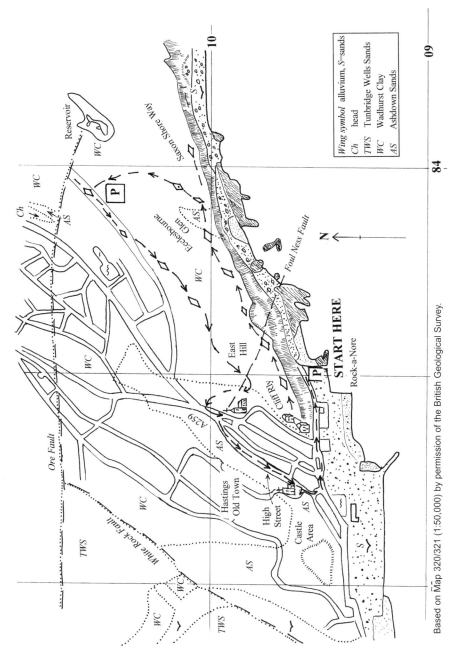

Based on Map 320/321 (1:50,000) by permission of the British Geological Survey.

16. HASTINGS & ECCLESBOURNE GLEN

OS 827095 (Hastings). Explorer map 124. Geological map: Hastings & Dungeness sheet 320/321 (1:50,000). 2 miles.

Drive east along the Hastings sea-front road called Rock-a-Nore Road, past the black 'net shops', the Fishermen's Museum and the Underwater World (a sea life centre) to the large car park at the end under the East Hill.

This walk is really in two parts, either of which might be sacrificed in the interest of time. The first half features stones used in the town's buildings, the second half the geology of the cliffs.

THE WALK

1. Start by ascending the East Hill either by the cliff railway or the neighbouring path. This leads to a wide open space on which there is an Iron Age Fort surrounded by a ditch and magnificent views over Hastings and out to sea. The town is entirely on Wealden Beds, but the exact distribution of outcrops of Ashdown Sands, Wadhurst Clay and Tunbridge Wells Sands is complex due to the intense faulting. The town fills the valley between the two escarpments exposed by the Bourne Stream, where it has cut its valley down into the Ashdown Sands.

Walk east along the path nearest to the sea until you can look down into Ecclesbourne Glen. Note that the massive sandstones of the upper Ashdown Sands are overlain by shales and sandstones of the Wadhurst Clay. The sandstone beds characteristically stand proud while the more easily eroded clays make gentler slopes. It is not possible to get to the beach down Ecclesbourne Glen, and we therefore now ascend the glen past Ecclesbourne Reservoir. Turn left into Barley Lane along the 1066 Country Walk, and follow this back to the town. Visit nearby All Saints Church.

This is one of the two churches of most geological interest. It stands at the north-east end of the medieval town. It is Perpendicular, built probably in the early 15th century. The west tower is mainly of sandstone but with patches and a course of flints and a diaper work on the summit battlements. The buttresses are cornered with limestone and infilled with flints.

Walk down the High Street, noting the variety of materials including brick, flint and local sandstone, passing Admiral Cloudesley Shovel's house on the right. A little further on, the house on the corner of Bourne Passage has its garden walled with local sandstone. Turn right along Courthouse Street, cross a road and see St Clement's Church on Croft Road, in the middle of the old town. It is Perpendicular and probably built after the French burning in 1377. The south-west tower is of sandstone and flint chequer, with building and buttress corners edged with limestone blocks.

Return to High Street, turn right and return to Rock-a-Nore car park.

2. Now walk along the coast eastwards. The lower part of the cliff is hidden under scree, although there is an in situ exposure at beach level where one can see carbonized wood in a silty mudstone. Small ferns have also been seen here.

The fine-grained sandstones and siltstones visible as boulders on the shore occasionally contain fossils of freshwater gastropods (snails), notably the 1cm long *Viviparus* and, on the bedding planes, the bivalve *Neomiodon* of similar size. The larger bivalves *Unio* and *Filosina* are present but less common. The oval-shaped ostracods *Cypridea* are also present on the bedding planes of thin shales but measure only about 1mm and so need to be examined with the help of a hand lens. Some are 'pimpled', some smooth.

Other fossils which have been found include caddis flies (*Trichoptera*), fish scales of *Lepidotes*, the scutes (horn-like plates) of turtle shells, the bones and teeth of crocodiles. The turtle shell scutes can be smooth or pimply, the plates from crocodile skin have circular dents, often exposed in pebble beds or on sandstone bedding planes.

Some of the rarer fossils found here include the finger bones of the pterosaur *Ornithochierus*, one of the largest of all flying reptiles, the teeth and bones of dinosaurs up to 10cm long, and the three-toed footprints of Iguanodon. On the beach there are some bluish-grey rocks containing strange, bulbous shapes. These are fallen blocks of Tilgate Stone from the Wadhurst Clay. This is a hard, fine-grained sandstone strongly cemented by calcium carbonate into tabular and nodular masses.

About ¼ mile (400m) east of Rock-a-Nore the horizontal strata of the cliff are displaced by the Foul Ness Normal Fault. However, this is obscured by a section of cliff which has slipped down to form a small plateau. Segments of the fossil horsetail *Equisetites* may be found in mud slides below this on the beach. These can be recognized by their striped appearance and tiny holes where leaves once grew around the stems.

Ecclesbourne Glen is a steep river valley carved out by the melt water from retreating glaciers. The attack of the sea has caused it here to be cut back into a 'hanging valley' with a 20-foot (6m) drop to the beach at the bottom.

Return to the car park from Ecclesbourne Glen. Note that the beach is largely made up of flint pebbles which do not originate here but have been washed along the beach from the chalk at Eastbourne, many miles to the west. Flints are often worth examining. Hollow ones sometimes contain very small, beautiful crystals of quartz, thought to have formed by replacement of delicate sponges.

It is strongly recommended to visit the Hastings Museum on John's Place, Bohemia Road (telephone 01424 718776; www.discoverhastings. co.uk). It has a good collection of the fossils to be found in the Chalk and Wealden beds. Note especially the impressions of Iguanodon footprints and the good collection of chalk fossils, including ammonites, echinoids, gastropods, bivalves, brachiopods, and bones of ichthyosaurs.

Cliffs in Ashdown Beds to the east of Hastings.

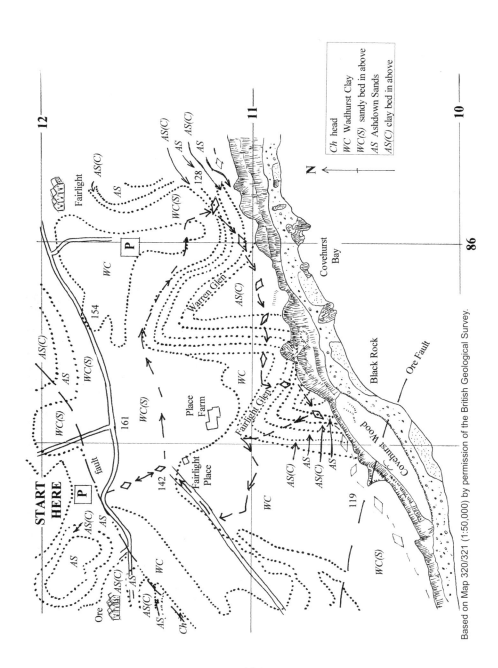

Based on Map 320/321 (1:50,000) by permission of the British Geological Survey.

17. HASTINGS COUNTRY PARK & FAIRLIGHT

OS 851110 (Hastings Country Park). Explorer map 124. Geological map: Hastings & Dungeness sheet 320/321(1:50,000). 2½ miles.
Start from Fairlight Road picnic site (847117).

This is a traverse of both Warren and Fairlight Glens. They have much the same geology. The level at the top is covered with Wadhurst Clay. The slopes down into the glens traverse Ashdown Sands from top to bottom. But these are not simple. The uppermost layers are sandy, then there is a zone of clay, another sandy layer and a second clayey

Hastings Country Park extends to the edge of the cliffs.

layer where it meets the beach. There is much slumped material on the headlands east and west of these two glens. The walk traverses the two glens and so passes over a somewhat bewildering alternation of sandy and clayey layers as shown on the map.

THE WALK

From the entrance to the car park cross the Hastings–Fairlight Road and follow the track opposite signposted to Fairlight Glen. After about 300 yards turn left along a path signposted to Warren Glen. At the end of the fenced path go ahead along a left field edge then across a shallow dip to a swing gate and on past a large notice saying 'Warren Glen'. Follow the path along the upper contours of Warren Glen passing two springs with some sandstone exposed in the slope above. Note the views to the sea.

Cross a field to a stile and turn right along a metalled drive, passing the old Coastguard Cottages and modern coastguard station on your right.

To the east of you are the extensive Fire Hills covered with gorse, heather, bracken and stunted trees indicative of the poor sandy soils. The name Fire Hills may derive from the colour of the gorse in bloom or relate to a time when it was set alight as a warning to sailors or smugglers. Note the view eastwards to Dungeness.

This is a coastal area and demonstrates the reaction of soft sandstones such as the Hastings Beds to marine attack. The cliffs are continually suffering undercutting and slump seawards as a result. The streams draining into the sea cut deep steep valleys. Examples are those cutting through the Hastings Country Park to Black Rock and, further east, Warren Glen debouching into Covehurst Bay. These streams may have originated when lands further north were under glaciers during the Ice Age. When these melted they gave much southward-flowing water.

Now go west through a swing gate along the coast walk called the Saxon Shore Way. You will pass a number of bollards. The first drop crosses the bottom of Warren Glen. Go left down a flight of steps. Cross a culverted stream at the bottom with a hydraulic ram and directly ahead climb a grassy strip which takes you up the other side of the glen.

At the top of the steepest part of the slope ignore the path to the right but go ahead to bollard 13, where you should bear half right up a flight of steps within a belt of woodland. At the top there is a natural sandstone bench. A path continues over the cliff top before dropping down another flight of steps into Fairlight Glen. At the T-junction at the foot of the steps turn left and cross a stream. It is sometimes possible to descend to the beach here, but the authorities have erected a fence (2003) and put a notice strongly discouraging such a descent on account of the danger of the steep slope and possible falling rocks. The material on the coast here is fine-grained sandstone and siltstone of the Ashdown Sands.

From bollard 10 ascend Fairlight Glen through Hastings Country Park to the Dripping Well at the top, and then turn sharp left and follow a footpath to the 1066 Country Walk. Turn right along this, and after 300 yards turn left along the track that leads back to the car park.

The East Hill, Hastings.

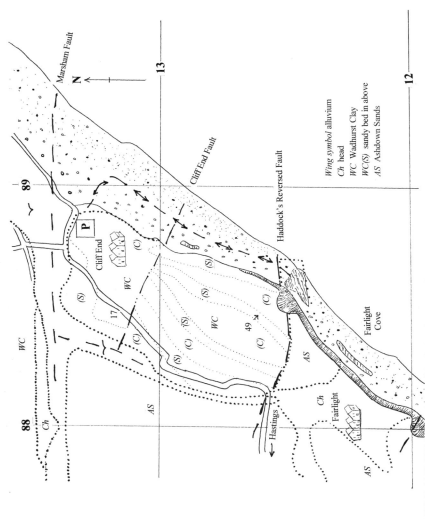

Marsham Fault

N

Cliff End Fault

Haddock's Reversed Fault

13

12

89

88

P

Cliff End

WC

(C)

(S)

17

(S)

(S)

(S)

(C)

WC

49

(C)

(C)

(C)

(C)

(S)

(S)

AS

AS

WC

AS

Ch

Ch

Fairlight Cove

Fairlight

← Hastings

Wing symbol alluvium
Ch head
WC Wadhurst Clay
WC(S) sandy bed in above
AS Ashdown Sands

Based on Map 320/321 (1:50,000) by permission of the British Geological Survey.

18. CLIFF END, FAIRLIGHT

OS 887133. Explorer map 124. Geological map: Hastings & Dungeness sheet 320/321 (1:50,000).

Drive from Hastings town centre north along the A259 to Ore. Fork right to Fairlight Village (Early English church: tall tower with beacon turret) and eventually Cliff End village. The car park is at 887133.

Walk 200 yards down to the sea front. Much care is needed when visiting this beach. To see the whole width, including almost all of the exposed sandstone, it is necessary to go at the lowest tide. These are semi-level stripped strata which have been exposed by erosion of the cliffs. Those nearest the sea are covered with seaweed, and it is therefore harder to see their form or fossils.

The best places to look for these are where the outcrops are high enough on the beach to prevent seaweed colonizing. Between these outcrops is sand and clay, the latter becoming very soft and miry, especially when the tide is rising or falling, so care is needed to avoid sinking when walking on it .

Wealden Sandstone is exposed between Fairlight and Hastings. Here it is mainly Ashdown Sands with a capping of Wadhurst Clay. Fossils from these rocks have been found at Fairlight Cove, including plant debris, bones, parts of turtles and fish scales. Many landslides are visible along the coast, some thought to be due to downslope flowage when the melting of the ice loosened and lubricated surface materials at the end of the Ice Age.

THE WALK

On the grey foreshore north-east of Cliff End (887130) is an outcrop of black peat 60cm thick. This contains the remains of an ancient forest, mainly of oak and hazel. It includes well preserved leaves, twigs and branches of oak and hazel ,with tree boles in growth position. Some Neolithic flint tools have also been found here. The forest dates from the end of the Ice Age more than 4,000 years ago when the sea level was lower. It grew before a rise in sea level reached the forest and drowned the trees. A recent drop in sea level has exposed them.

Cliff End, looking west.

Walk south-west along the beach observing the cliff line. Although the geological map shows the overlying Wadhurst Clay Beds, the cliff is mostly massive well-jointed Ashdown Sandstones, gently dipping north-eastwards. The first cliffs are the Cliff End Sandstone, 33ft (10m) thick. This lies about 1m above the Top Ashdown Pebble Bed and is a prominent feature of the cliff tops and abandoned sea cliffs at the base of the Wadhurst Clay. The bulk of the latter, some 36–60m of strata, is largely interlaminated grey-green shales and siltstones with a few bands of nodular clay ironstone and thin shelly limestone. After about 150 yards there is a small normal fault called the Cliff End Fault.

Note the way the sea erodes into the vertical joints in the rock of the cliff. Beware of the instability of these cliffs.

The cliff face also shows cross-bedded sands and silts with some visible hollows caused by channels and filled with the alluvium they once carried. The lower part may have been deposited in a delta, the upper part in a river valley. The Cliff End Bone Bed is about 1m above the Pebble Bed and is up to 20cm thick. Because it is in the upper part of the cliff it is best studied from fallen blocks on the foreshore. It is a carbonate-cemented coarse sandstone containing pebbles of quartz, chert and clay ironstone concretions. It also contains fish scales, teeth and bones, together with shark and reptile remains.

Note the relation between the cliff and the beach boulders. The latter contain fine lamination, ripple marks, cross bedding, plant fragments and shelly beds of fresh water molluscs. In places there are small root-like iron stains vertical to the strata which may once have marked roots. Significantly, Iguanodon fossils and footprints have been found on the beach which are believed to have fallen from a sandy bed in the Ashdown Sands of the cliff face. Their placement in this sandstone bed suggests that they lived by a rapidly flowing stream beside clayey swamps. As you walk westwards you are moving down the succession due to the slight dip to the north-north-east associated with the Fairlight Anticline. Crocodile fossils have also been found on the beach, and on the rock surface washed by the sea there are three-toed footprints of the theropod reptile.

About 500 yards beyond the Cliff End Fault is Haddock's Reversed Fault. This intersects the cliff about 200 yards north-east of Haddock's Cottages (886125), and the fault plane dips 60 degrees to the south-south-west. The material on the northern side of the fault has been downthrown about 60m. The low ground caused by erosion along the fault gives some access to the beach. Immediately southwest of it, the point at 885125 is caused by an outcrop of harder rock. This is because the fault has dropped a hard ferruginous sandstone down to beach level, which makes a distinctive wave-cut platform. It contains many plant remains, including some rootlets possibly in the position of growth.

West of this point is Fairlight Cove. If time is available it may be of interest to continue the walk to the middle of the cove, because there is considerable further rock exposure on the beach.

As there is no access to the top of the cliff it is necessary to return to the car park along the beach.

A remnant of the 4,000-year-old forest exposed on the beach.

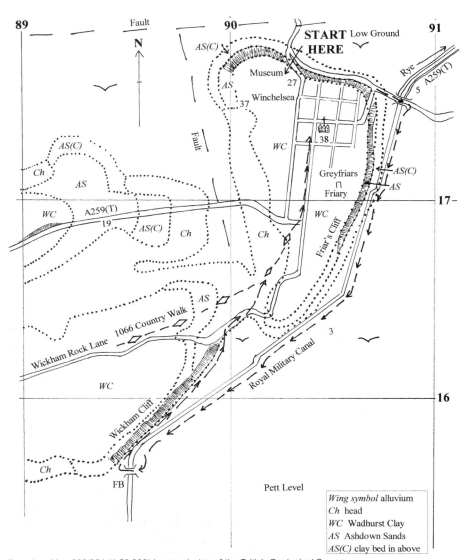

Based on Map 320/321 (1:50,000) by permission of the British Geological Survey.

112

19. WINCHELSEA & PETT LEVEL

OS 905175 (Winchelsea). Explorer map 125. Geological map: Hastings & Dungeness sheet 320/321 (1:50,000). 3 miles.
Park in Winchelsea at the National Trust centre, where there is a museum.

You can see old sea cliffs around Pett Level, Winchelsea, Rye and Appledore. The best exposures are in the lanes around Winchelsea (902171, 902169, 902162 and 907172). These show the upper sandstones of the Ashdown Sands overlain by thin Wadhurst Clay containing the basal Wadhurst siderite ironstone. On top of these we find the lower part of the Cliff End Sandstone.

Winchelsea stands on an island of Ashdown Sands capped by Wadhurst Clay. It is surrounded on three sides by Pett Level, a wide flat area of reclaimed marshland on clay in the Wealden Series that stretches about 25 miles (40km) north-east to Hythe. The area suffered repeated submergence up to the cliff line during the Ice Age, and this accounts for the cliffs which encircle the town as well as Cadborough Cliff to the north (905195) and Wickham Cliff to the south (895157). Shingle spits grew out from Fairlight in the south-west and Hythe in the north-east. Aided by a drop in sea level, these cut off the bay from the sea and allowed it to become filled with river-borne sediment. At one time it supported forest, remnants of which can still be seen low on the foreshore at Pett Level (890131). The trees were mainly oak and hazel.

Perhaps the most dramatic events occurred in the thirteenth century when a series of great storms in the Channel led to the breaching of the barrier shingle ridges and the diversion of the estuary of the river Rother. This destroyed the port of old Winchelsea, which now lies buried under the alluvium east of the present estuary of the Rother

The present town is the new Winchelsea. It was built under Edward I from 1283 in the grid pattern which still survives. It was, however, never successfully developed as a port, and the squares were never completely filled with building, mainly because of this change. It has three medieval gateways and many charming houses. Its central church, St Thomas, is 14th century.

The parish church of St Thomas, Winchelsea.

THE WALK

First visit the church and the museum (telephone 01797 226382; www.sussexmuseums.co.uk/Winchelsea.htm). The former was originally intended to be much larger, but only the chancel and its two side chapels remain intact. The outstanding visual feature is the stained-glass windows by Douglas Strachan (1928–1933). It is largely built of local sandstone with limestone used for edges and corners. Inside it uses Sussex marble for the four subsidiary circling shafts around the tall limestone pillars.

Go east out of the town through the Strand Gate, beside which is the steep drop of the former sea cliffs which circle the town. To the north across the valley of the river Brede you can see another: Cadborough Cliff.

Follow the A259 across the bridge over the Royal Military Canal.

Immediately turn right off this along the path down the eastern side of the canal, called both the Saxon Shore Way and the Royal Military Canal Path. For the first half mile this runs parallel to the Winchelsea sea cliff on the right. The canal, constructed during the Napoleonic wars, is a good habitat for swans and other birds. On the left, to the east, note Pett Level, a flat alluvial plain of reclaimed marshland at about sea level. It is floored with river and sea-deposited clay which is very fertile. It requires drainage, as can be seen from the network of ditches. It bears abundant and varied crops of cereals and also cattle and sheep.

About a mile further on the canal bends to the left. Cross the footbridge here and take the path up to the north, with woodland concealing Wickham Cliff, a former sea cliff on your left cut in Ashdown Sands. Turn right at the road (Wickham Rock Lane), and after 150 yards, where the road bends to the right, go straight on along the path 1066 Country Walk to re-enter Winchelsea from the south through the New Gate.

A bridge over the Royal Military Canal.

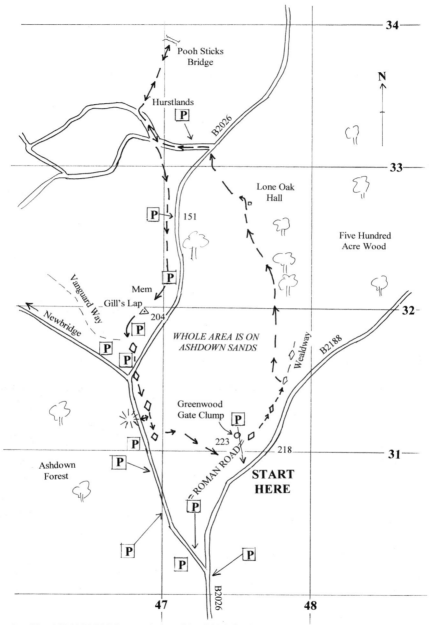

Based on Map 303 (1:50,000) by permission of the British Geological Survey.

20. CROWBOROUGH COMMON

OS 473303. Explorer map 135. Geological map: Tunbridge Wells sheet 303 (1:50,000). 3¼ miles or 3½ miles if Pooh Bridge is included.

Start from the car park at 476308 on the B2188 west of Crowborough, or from one of the other car parks nearby.

The high ridges of the inner Weald make one of the most beautiful and distinctive landscapes of south-eastern England. The distant views from open ground create the impression of unbroken forest, but it has been much altered by local agriculture and mining for marl and iron ore. Traditionally the forest has been preserved because of its uneven topography, its poor sandy soils and its consequent remoteness from the regions of dense settlement in Roman, Saxon and later time.

Ashdown Forest from East Grinstead by F W Griggs. [Lucas (1935) p. 403]

Crowborough Common.

The area of this walk is in the east of Ashdown Forest, where the Roman road from London to Chichester strikes across its crest from Maresfield to Hartfield. There are fairly extensive remains of former iron workings from the Ashdown Sands and the lower beds of the Wadhurst Clay.

THE WALK
Go west from the car park for a few yards to the Wealdway. Here it follows a Roman road. Go north along one of the several rather ill-defined lines of tracks used by many walkers and riders.

The whole area of the walk is on Ashdown Sands. Underfoot there is fine gravel and sand and occasionally the underlying rock appears at the surface. When it is red it means that iron in hematite form (Fe_2O_3) is colouring it, where yellow, limonite ($Fe_2O_3 2H_2O$). The latter indicates more moisture at the time of formation. Occasionally it is bluish. This is due to earlier formation of FeO under anaerobic conditions when bacteria remove oxygen from the iron oxide.

The circle of trees on the left called Greenwood Gate Clump approximately coincides with the highest point in Ashdown Forest (732ft; 223m). This was planted by the Duke of Dorset in 1816 to give cover to game birds. It is not always easy to distinguish because of the surrounding trees and gorse.

Continue north along the Weald Way, which here follows the line of the Roman road. Gill's Lap (trig pillar) becomes visible to the west. Continue along the Weald Way until you reach the Five Hundred Rough at its meeting with the Five Hundred Acre Wood. Tracks are here confusing, but aim to continue down the valley, keeping the stream on your left, until after about 500 yards you pass Lone Oak Hall and pick up a tarmac road. Follow this down, passing a small waterfall near the bridge over the stream, after another 300 yards joining the B2026 at Chuck Hatch.

Go right for a few yards and then take the lane to the left for 300 yards to Hurstlands.

Optional diversion to Pooh Sticks Bridge:
After about 200 yards down this road enter the Pooh car park. Take the walk out of it signed 'Take your valuables with you'. This can be muddy in wet weather. After about 300 yards you rejoin the road. Keep straight on along it for a few yards and then turn right along the marked path to Pooh Bridge – which is about 500 yards further on. Those familiar with A.A. Milne's books about Christopher Robin and Winnie the Pooh will remember the story in *The House at Pooh Corner* of Pooh and his friends dropping sticks on the upstream side of the bridge and seeing which one appears first on the downstream side. This game of Pooh Sticks is included in several of E.H. Shepard's attractive illustrations.

Return to Hurstlands, and follow the road back towards Chuck Hatch. After 200 yards turn left at a road junction and almost immediately take a track leading right southwards towards Gill's Lap. Continue along this keeping the B2026 on your left until your reach the charming memorial to Milne and Shepard. It gives a fine view towards the north. A hundred yards further on you reach the trig pillar at Gill's Lap (469320). This also gives fine views across the clay vales to the North and South Downs.

This open area was grazed but this has declined so that gorse and other vegetation is now encroaching.

Note that the village of Newbridge (456328) 1 mile (1.6km) to the west had the most important forge in Ashdown Forest. Its site still forms a distinctive feature in the landscape with its hammer pond and winding channels, which supplied water to the water wheels, the scattered cottages and the patchwork of enclosed fields on the edge of the wide bracken-clad slopes that climb to the summit of the forest.

From Gill's Lap cross the B2026 and follow the Vanguard Way southeast back to the upper end of a large valley. This is the source of one of the streams draining into the Medway. The view here reveals characteristic sandstone country with its surface drainage and relatively deep valley incisions into the landscape. At the head of the valley, cross the road again to the high point labelled as having a panoramic view on the Explorer map. It is now a circular plinth without any inscription. It is just north of the car park at 469311 with a wooden board labelled 'Four Counties' which, with small detours to avoid low trees, gives magnificent views in all directions, terminated only by the chalk hills that encircle the Weald.

Recross the road to the Vanguard Way, and take the path back to the car park, keeping the Greenwood Gate clump of trees on your left.

Sandstone exposure on Crowborough Common.

Glossary

abacus: flat slab forming the top of a capital.

alluvium: sedimentary deposits resulting from the action of rivers.

ammonite: marine dwelling creature with a circular rotating shell whose lobes and saddles are more or less finely separated.

anticlinal fold: a fold forming part of an anticline.

anticline: an arched upfold in the earth's crust.

aragonite: carbonate of lime in mineral form ($CaCO_3$).

bailey: area round the motte or keep of a castle, defended by a wall and ditch.

baluster: a pillar or pedestal of bellied form.

bastide (French): a fortified town built to defend a strategic location.

belemnite: marine creature whose internal shell is largely a solid cigar-shaped or dart-shaped 'guard' of calcite with a conical chambered hollow at one end.

bioturbation: the breakdown and reworking of sediment by the action of its contained organisms, especially earthworms.

bivalve: a mollusc having a shell consisting of two lateral plates or valves joined together by an elastic ligament at the hinge.

brachiopod: a class of molluscs with symmetrical bivalve shells with a hole near the apex for a 'foot.'

brickearth: The windblown fine-textured soils which have been re-sorted and re-deposited by water, frequently in old river terraces.

cambering: the downward bending or draping over of a hard horizontal rock at the edge of its outcrop at the side of a valley.

capital: head or crowning feature of a column or pilaster.

carstone: a hard ferruginous sandstone of the Lower Cretaceous.

cella: the part enclosed within the walls of an ancient temple.

chert: a hard rock of opaline and/or chalcedonic silica. It is black or dull in character and fractures along flat planes in contrast to flint, which has conchoidal fracture and which itself is a variety of chert.

clay-with-flints: a deposit containing a mixture of clay and flints.

clunch: stiff clay.

coccolith: small discoid plate which once built up the calcareous sheath of unicellar planktonic algae.

concretions: more or less spherical or irregular masses of material different from the surrounding rock brought together by percolating waters.

conglomerate: a sedimentary rock consisting of pebbles and rock fragments cemented together by calcium carbonate, silica, or another binder.

consequent (river): a river whose direction of flow is controlled by the original slope of the land.

coombe: a hollow in a hillside, generally the unwatered portion of a valley which forms its continuation beyond and above the most elevated spring which issues into it.

coombe rock: a structureless mass of unstratified rubble brought by gravity which
fills a coombe. (See also *head*.)
cross bedding: the disposition of laminations within a rock stratum transverse or
obliquely inclined to the main stratification of the bedding planes.
cryoturbation: frost action which churns, heaves and structurally modifies the soil
and subsoil.
cuesta: an asymmetrical ridge produced by differential erosion of dipping strata.

diaper work: repetitive surface decoration of lozenges or squares.
dip: the angle which a bedding plane makes with a horizontal plane, measured in
a direction perpendicular to the strike of the rock strata.
dipslope: the surface slope down a dipping bed.
dip stream: stream flowing down dip.
doline: circular hollow or depression usually floored with clay formed by solution
of underlying rock.
downthrow: measurement of the drop of rock on one side of a fault.

echinoid: sea anemone or sea urchin.
encaustic: fixed by burning.
erratic: large detached block moved from its place of origin by ice.
escarpment: any line of cliffs or abrupt slope breaking the continuity of a surface.

fault, normal: fault inclined towards the upthrown side.
fault, reversed: fault inclined towards the downthrown side.
ferruginous: partaking of iron.
flint: a variety of chert in irregular, usually bulbous, nodules found in the chalk.
foreset beds: inclined beds built forward in a deltaic deposit each above and in
front of the previous one, as in an embankment built by tipping.
fret: a shallow and narrow recess in an escarpment.

gastropod: snail or other sea or land creature with shells of spiral type.
geode: a hollow cavity in a rock, almost spherical in shape in which inward-pointing
crystals line its interior walls.
glauconite: a green hydrous silicate of iron and potassium characteristic of the
Greensand formation.
goniatite: a coiled ammonite in which the sutures between internal chambers
have angular zigzags.
greensand: a sand or sandstone with a high proportion of the mineral glauconite.
gypsum: a white soft hydrate of calcium sulphate, $CaSO_4.2H_2O$.

hanger: a local term for a beechwood on a steep chalk slope in southern England.
head: a Pleistocene accumulation of sharp, angular local rocks, coarse close to the
hills but smaller and mixed with fine material further away.
honeycomb weathering: weathering which produces the superficial appearance of
an enlarged honeycomb.

ichthyosaur: a sea dwelling reptile.

iguanodon: a colossal bird-hipped lizard with three large toes.

inlier: an exposure of rocks which is completely surrounded by younger strata, resulting especially from the breaching and erosion of an anticlinal structure.

karren: all microforms on limestone, ranging in size from a few millimetres to several metres.

lagoon: a coastal stretch of shallow salt-water virtually cut off from the open sea by a beach.

lamellibranch: mollusc with shell consisting of two hinged valves, also known as pelecypod.

lapiés: a synonym for karren.

limestone: a rock consisting chiefly of carbonate of lime ($CaCO_3$).

loess: an unstratified, homogeneous, fine-grained brickearth, probably the result of wind deposition from materials exposed to deflation after glacial retreat.

lynchet: an artificial cultivation terrace cut into a hillside more or less parallel with the contours. Widespread in the English chalklands.

manger: an armchair-shaped recess in a chalk escarpment.

marl: a mixed rock containing clay minerals and aragonite or calcite, usually with lesser components such as silt.

meander: a sinuosity or loop-like bend in a river, characterized by a river-cliff or bluff on the outside of the curve and a gently shelving slope on the inner side.

Mesozoic: of the middle range of strata, younger than Palaeozoic but older than Cenozoic..

motte: a steep mound forming the main feature of 11th and 12th century castles.

nodule: a small lump of mineral or stony substance occurring in a bed of rock or concretionary or other formation.

ogee: a double curve, bending first one way and then the other.

ostracod: a crustacean in which a small oval bivalved carapace completely encloses the body.

outcrop: 1. that part of the earth's surface on which a particular type of rock occurs without covering.

2. the area where a particular rock body emerges at the earth's surface.

outlier: an outcrop of a younger rock completely surrounded by older rocks.

Palaeozoic: the first main group of fossil-bearing rocks in the earth's crust, following the Proterozoic and preceding the Mesozoic.

pelecypod: synonym for lamellibranch.

pier: strong, solid support, usually round or square in section.

pitch (of rocks): the dip along the crest of an anticline or the trough of a syncline.

Pleistocene: the early part of the Quaternary period which experienced the Ice Age.

plesiosaur: long-necked marine dinosaur.

plunge: the diving effect of an anticline whose axial surface has become bent over.

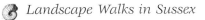

Primary: a synonym for Palaeozoic.

purbeck marble: a polishable limestone from the uppermost strata of the Jurassic, named from Purbeck, Dorset.

Quaternary: the last of the periods of geological deposition, following the Cenozoic. It includes the Pleistocene Ice Age.

ram, hydraulic: an automatic apparatus by which a descending stream of water is made to raise by its own momentum a proportion of its mass to a required height.

re-entrant: a steep and short valley cut back into high ground.

rife: a local name for a small watercourse in the coastal plain of Sussex.

sandstone: a consolidated sand.

sarsen: boulders of hard silicified sandstone scattered over the chalk of south-east England. Also called greywethers.

scarp: see *escarpment*.

shale: laminated clay hardened into rock.

siderite: an iron ore composed of ferrous carbonate ($FeCO_3$).

silicification: the process by which silica replaces existing structures or minerals.

solifluxion: the downslope flowage of masses of surface waste saturated with water.

sphaerosiderite: siderite in fibrous radial knobs.

spicule: a small spike.

spit: a narrow and elongated accumulation of sand and shingle projecting into a large body of water, usually the sea.

strike: the direction, at any point on a structural surface, especially a bedding plane, of a horizontal line drawn on that surface. It is at right angles to the dip.

strike stream: a stream flowing parallel to the direction of strike.

syncline: a trough-fold in which the strata dip inwards towards a central axis.

talus: material, detached by weathering, which has accumulated in piles at the foot of a slope. Also called scree.

Tertiary: a synonym for Cenozoic.

undercutting: the erosive action of a river or an ocean wave at the base of a cliff.

underfit river: a stream that is too small for the valley it occupies.

undersapping; the action of water in undermining the rocks above its point of emergence from them.

voussoirs: wedge-shaped stones forming an arch.

windgap: a valley or col in a ridge though which no stream passes.

Bibliography

Allen, John (1999) *The Sussex Border Path: Day Walks and Circular Routes,* Sigma Press, Wilmslow, Cheshire.

Allen, P (1958) *Geology of the Central Weald: the Hastings Beds,* Geologists' Association Guide No 24, London.

Bell, Richard (1996) *Yorkshire Rock: A Journey Through Time,* British Geological Survey, An Earthwise Publication, Nottingham.

Bristow, C R, Bazley, R A et al. (1972) *Geology of the Country around Royal Tunbridge Wells,* Explanation of one-Inch Geological Sheet 303, New Series, Memoirs of the Geological Survey of England and Wales, Natural Environmental Research Council, Institute of Geological Sciences, HMSO, London.

Brooks, Ken (2001) *Geology and Fossils of the Hastings Area,* published by Ken Brooks and printed by D C Graphics Limited, Bexhill-on-Sea.

British Museum (Natural History) (1975) *British Cenozoic Fossils (Tertiary and Quaternary)* Fifth Edition, London.

Castleden, Rodney (1996) *Classic Landforms of the Sussex Coast,* The Geographical Association, Sheffield.

Davies, G M (1939) *Geology of London and South-East England,* Thomas Murby, London.

Edmunds, F H (1954) *The Wealden District,* 3rd Edition, British Regional Geology, Department of Scientific and Industrial Research, Geological Survey and Museum, HMSO, London.

Evans, I O (1973) *The Observer's Book of Geology,* Frederick Warne & Co. Ltd., London.

Gibbons, Wes (1981) *The Weald,* Unwin Paperbacks, London.

Holmes, A (1956), *Principles of Physical Geology,* Thomas Nelson, London.

Jenner, Lorna, Lawton, Eila, Fernandez, Sandra et al. High Weald Forum (1999) *Along and Around the High Weald Landscape Trail,* Uckfield, Sussex.

Jones, David K C (1981) *Southeast and Southern England,* The Geomorphology of the British Isles, Methuen, London.

Lobeck, A K (1939) *Geomorphology,* McGraw Hill, New York.

Lucas, Edward Verrall (1935) *Highways and Byways in Sussex,* Macmillan, London.

Mantell, G (1827) Illustrations of the Geology of Sussex, London

Millmore, Paul (1990) *South Downs Way,* National Trail Guide, Aurum Press Ltd., London.

Millward, Roy & Robinson, Adrian (1973) *South East England: The Channnel Coastlands,* Landscapes of Britain, Macmillan, London.

Mortimore, Rory N (1997) *The Chalk of Sussex and Kent,* Geologists' Association Guide No. 57, London.

Nairn, Ian and Pevsner, Nikolaus (2001) *The Buildings of England: Sussex,* Penguin Books, London.Natural History Museum (2001) *British Mesozoic Fossils,* 6th edition, London.

Osborne White, H J (1928) *The Geology of the Country near Hastings and Dungeness* (Explanation of Sheets 320 and 321), Memoirs of the Geological Survey, England, HMSO, London.

Osborne White, H J (1926) *The Geology of the Country near Lewes* (Explanation of Sheet 319), Memoirs of the Geological Survey, England, HMSO, London.

Osborne White, H J (1924) *The Geology of the Country Near Brighton and Worthing (Explanation of Sheets 318 and 333)*, Memoirs of the Geological Survey of England and Wales, HMSO, London.

Owen, Ellis & Smith, Andrew B. (eds.) (1987) *Fossils of the Chalk, Palaeontological Field Guides to Fossils*, No. 2. London.

Perkins, Ben (2000) *Waterside Walks in Sussex,* Countryside Books, Newbury, Berkshire.

Perkins, Ben (1998) *Village Walks in East Sussex,* Countryside Books, Newbury, Berkshire.

Perkins, Ben (2001) *Classic Walks in Sussex,* S. B. Publications, Seaford.

Reid, Clement, with contributions by Lamplugh, G W and Jukes-Browne, A J (1903) *The Geology of the Country Near Chichester (Explanation of Sheet 317),* Memoirs of the Geological Survey of England and Wales, HMSO, London.

Robinson, D A & Williams, R B G (1984) *Classic Landforms of the Weald,* Landform Guides No 4, Geographical Association, Sheffield.

Ruffell, Alastair, Ross, Andrew & Taylor, Kevin (1996) *Early Cretaceous Environments of the Weald,* Geologists' Association Guide No. 55, edited by J T Greensmith, London.

Shephard-Thorn, E R and Wymer, J J (1977) *Southeast England and the Thames Valley: Guidebook for Excursion A5,* International Union for Quaternary Research (INQUA), Geo. Abstracts Limited, University of East Anglia, Norwich.

Spence, Keith (1999) *The Companion Guide to Kent and Sussex,* Boydell and Brewer, Woodbridge, Suffolk..

Steers, J A (1964) *The Coastline of England and Wales,* Cambridge University Press.

Steers, J A (1966) *The English Coast and the Coast of Wales,* The Fontana Library, London.

Trueman, A E (1971) *Geology and Scenery in England and Wales,* revised by J B Whittow and J R Hardy, Pelican, London.

Vesey, Barbara (ed.) (1998) *The Hidden Places of Sussex*, Travel Publishing, Aldermaston, Berks.

Watkins, Alfred (1997) *The Old Straight Track,* Abacus, Little Brown & Co., London.

Whittow, John B. (1984) *The Penguin Dictionary of Physical Geography,* Penguin Books Ltd., Harmondsworth, Middlesex.

Woodcock, Roy (1998) *A Year of Walks in Sussex,* Sigma Press, Wilmslow, Cheshire.

CONVERSION TABLE, IMPERIAL/METRIC

1 inch = 2.54cm	1cm = 0.394 inches
1 foot = 30.5cm	
1 yard = 91cm	1 metre = 1.094 yards
1 mile = 1.609km	1 kilometre = 0.621 miles; 1094 yards

Acknowledgements

My thanks are due to Steve Benz for the conception of this book, to Lindsay Woods for its publication and to David Arscott for editing the text. I also thank the following for permission to reproduce illustrations: Roy Millward and Adrian Robinson, for the figures on pages 27, 30, 33 and 35, Mr Julian Porter of the Bexhill Museum for the figure on page 11 (bottom), Mr F A Gibbons for the figure on page 14 and the Geologists' Association for the figures on page 11 (top) and 13. A special thank you to Mr Daniel Southern for the photographs on pages 59, 74 and 75.

Geographical boundaries on maps are reproduced by permission of the British Geological Survey © NERC. All rights reserved. IPR/50-18C.

About the author

Dr Colin Mitchell is a lover of the Sussex countryside, in which he has spent most of his holidays since childhood and in which he has retained a permanent base. He took his first degree in geography at Oxford, and then worked for about ten years as a soil surveyor, mainly in North Africa and the Middle East. His doctorate on a study of terrain was from Cambridge University. He then lectured in physical geography at Reading University until retirement, accompanying and following this with consultancies in the interpretation and application of aerial and satellite photography to the study of landforms.

He is the author of three books and co-author of three more, and has written a number of chapters in other books and scientific papers.

He and his wife Clemency have four children and five grandchildren.

Other walks books from S.B. Publications

Classic Walks in Sussex (Ben Perkins)
On Foot on the High Weald (Ben Perkins)
Walking in West Sussex (Tony Oldfield)
Walks in Ashdown Forest (Christine Baldwin)
West Sussex Walks (Sandy Hernu)
Wildlife Walks in the Cuckmere Valley (Patrick Coulcher)
On Foot on the West Sussex Downs (Ben Perkins)
The South Downs Way (David Harrison)

We publish a wide range of local interest books on Sussex.
For a free catalogue please write to:
S.B. Publications, c/o 19 Grove Road, Seaford, East Sussex BN25 1TP
or access our website on www.sbpublications.co.uk